AGRICULTURE AND URBAN GROWTH

Agriculture and Urban Growth

A STUDY OF THE COMPETITION FOR RURAL LAND

by

G. P. WIBBERLEY

B.Sc. (Hons.), M.S., PH.D., HON. A.T.P.I.

*Reader
in Agriculture with special reference to Agricultural Economics
in the University of London
and
Head of the Department of Economics,
Wye College (University of London)*

London
MICHAEL JOSEPH

First published by
MICHAEL JOSEPH LTD
26 Bloomsbury Street
London, W.C.1
1959

Set and printed in Great Britain by Unwin Brothers Ltd.
at the Gresham Press, Woking, in Times type, eleven
point leaded, on paper made by Henry Bruce at Currie,
Midlothian, and bound by James Burn at Esher

To the late
A. W. ASHBY, M.A.
Professor of Agricultural Economics at
the University College of Wales, Aberystwyth
and, later, Director of the Agricultural
Economics Research Institute
University of Oxford
who stimulated my interest
in both land and people

CONTENTS

PREFACE

In many countries there is a problem of allocating scarce resources in land among many competing uses. With rising standards of living there is always a heavy flow of people from rural areas into towns and cities and the competition between urban and rural land uses is, therefore, intensified. The problem is seen at its greatest in countries with a large population relative to their land areas. A unique example is Great Britain, particularly as the country is not self-sufficient in food and is vulnerable, therefore, in times of international crisis.

In all countries, at some stage in their development, this urbanisation gives rise, first, to agitation and, later, to legislation to control changes in land use so that action by the individual does not prejudice conditions of work and living for other individuals or the community at large. At this stage, also, considerable controversy usually arises as to the impact of urban growth on agricultural and rural conditions and on national food supplies.

An attempt is made in this book to present a factual account of how the land surface of Great Britain is being used and the real effects of the competition of expanding towns for agricultural land. A method is suggested of assessing the value of alternative sites of differing agricultural values in relation to differences in the cost of urban development and its practical use is demonstrated. Possibilities of replacing the food now produced on the land earmarked for urban purposes are later discussed in relation to imports of food from abroad and the gaining of new land in the hills and in the lowlands of this country.

The results suggest that comparative analyses of the costs and benefits likely from such actions can and ought to be made. At the present time many of our rural and urban land use policies do not make economic sense and our methods of balancing up competing claims for rural land need to be made more systematic. It is hoped that some of the facts given and methods suggested will be of value in this connection.

Research on these problems has been carried out during recent years by a small team in the Department of Agricultural Economics at Wye College, University of London, which has been partly financed by a grant from Counterpart Funds made available by co-operative arrangements between the United States and British Governments. The team, working under my direction, has consisted of:

> J. T. Ward, B.Sc., B.Litt.,
> R. H. Best, M.Sc.,
> G. J. Tyler, M.Sc.,

and, part time,

> R. Gray, B.Sc.,
> B. R. Davidson, M.Sc., Ph.D.

The scope and character of the investigations, together with the concept of food replacement, originated in my paper 'The Challenge of Rural Land Losses' delivered to the Royal Society of Arts in 1954. As the research has developed, members of the team have worked on specific projects. Mr. R. H. Best has been primarily concerned with building up the picture of land use changes in this country. Mr. J. T. Ward has evolved a method of measurement applicable to siting problems and looked into the food import situation. Dr. Davidson, as part of his Ph.D. studies, contributed a measure of the agricultural output of the hills and uplands of Great Britain. Mr. G. J. Tyler investigated aspects of land improvement in the lowlands concerned with coastal reclamation, drainage and derelict woodland, and Mr. Gray collected information on opencast mineral workings. I am grateful to these colleagues for their enthusiasm, skill and integrity over a wide field of investigation in which little previous work had been done.

I have tried to present the facts and arguments of this book in a simple and readable manner, and in this writing I have been greatly helped by the comments of various colleagues at Wye College, especially Messrs. Best and Ward. Mr. J. H. Kirk, C.B.E., M.A., of the Ministry of Agriculture, Fisheries and Food, and Mr. Dunstan Skilbeck, C.B.E.,

M.A., Principal of Wye College, have also been kind enough to read and comment on many parts of the manuscript.

Finally, I would like to thank the Ministry of Agriculture, Fisheries and Food for arranging the research grant and providing important information. The Ministry of Housing and Local Government has also placed at our disposal certain land-use information from Development Plans. Professor W. Ellison has kindly allowed the reproduction of the tabular material given in Tables 12, 13 and 14.

Wye College,   G. P. WIBBERLEY
University of London,
September 1959.

ILLUSTRATIONS

DIAGRAMS

TABLES

Chapter 1 The Desire for Land

THIS book deals with land and some of the problems which have arisen in man's competition for it. Land, as defined for our purpose, constitutes the surface of the earth with all its natural and human attributes, the space directly above it, the climate that it enjoys and the sub-surface with its mineral deposits. Many people, therefore, need land—to grow food for themselves and for others, to mine for minerals of economic value and as a site on which to build their houses, factories, shops and other private and community structures.

In the production of wealth it is customary to talk of men's organisation of land, labour and capital. As man learns better methods of exploiting natural resources and of using his own hands and brains, the increase in wealth begins to rely not so much on land but more and more on the skilled use of people and the ample provision of capital, especially in the form of machines. It is true that the value of land has risen with the appreciation of wages and salaries, stocks and shares, but there has been a gradual though important trend for land to become relatively less and less important as a factor in the production of material wealth. Even in food production man is increasingly able to dominate soils, both in his methods of cultivation and in the provision of the food elements needed by plants and animals. The inherent fertility of land is becoming less important overall and variations in fertility more easily corrected. Yet the location of a piece of land and the local climate which it enjoys or suffers are of increasing importance in any use and are reflected in great differences in land values. Contrast the sums paid for a rocky site in New York with the value of similar rocky land in Mid Wales or for heavy clay land in the heart of London as against the clay of rural Essex.

Though land has fallen behind labour and capital in its relative importance in agricultural production and as an element in food cost, all three have increased in absolute importance. As national and local populations increase, more food-producing land is wanted and greater production is asked from existing cultivated land. But this need for extra food may not cause a directly proportional extra demand for cultivated land. More people in a country or region may not be associated with more purchasing power for food but only the sharing out of the same food amongst more mouths. More mouths to feed, however, may also be accompanied by more purchasing power and a change in diet away from foods like potatoes which need little land for their production in favour of those such as meat and cows' milk which use relatively more land.

Even within a particular area or country the amount and character of food-producing land can vary over a relatively few years if major changes of diet occur either voluntarily or under pressure. This happened in the United Kingdom during World War II, when the character of home-produced food changed substantially. Of the total output of home-produced calories in the years 1936 to 1939 only 18 per cent came from cereals. This proportion had risen to 43 per cent by 1943–4 and then dropped, after hostilities ended, to 28 per cent by 1949–50. These changes were accompanied by changes of an opposite nature in products such as meat, milk and eggs.[1] Thus, with no major changes in the total population of the country but through restrictions on the amount and character of food to be eaten, the area of land required to supply one British person changed appreciably during this period of time. More than half as many people again were supported by each 100 acres of cultivated land in 1943–4 in comparison with the years immediately before World War II.

The relationship between the number of people to be fed and the amount of land needed to feed them is therefore not a straightforward one. It is highly complex and involves consideration of the diet which people are prepared to accept, personal incomes, the relative prices for food, other necessities and luxuries, political circumstances, the fertility and

[1] Wyllie, J., 'Land Requirements for the Production of Human Food,' Studies in Rural Land Use, Report No. 1, Wye College, 1954, pp. 12 and 13.

Table 1

CHANGES IN THE AREA OF LAND NEEDED TO FEED ONE
PERSON IN THE UNITED KINGDOM

Year	Acres of home-production required to feed one person	Persons fed per 100 acres of crops and grass
1936–9 (average)	1·85	54
1943–4	1·15	87
1947–8	1·54	65
1949–50	1·28	78

flexibility of use of cultivated land and the availability of food from other areas or countries.

Yet there are limits to the flexibility and variation in the relationship between the food needs of a person and the area of land needed to produce the food to satisfy these needs. Though there are forces making for reductions in the area of land required, such as increased crop and livestock yields, there are other trends which lead to the need for greater areas of food-producing land. An important one is the change in people's food habits which occur as standards of living rise and people are able to spend more on food. At low standards of living people exist on diets consisting mainly of cereals and bulk vegetables. The protein part of the diet is usually low, and is obtained from products using relatively small areas of land, such as peas and beans of various kinds, the ubiquitous domestic fowl which scratches a precarious living from its day of hatching to the final end in the cooking pot, the domestic pig fed on crop and domestic residues, and fish obtained from fresh and salt waters. As purchasing power increases, total consumption of food naturally increases until physical satisfaction is reached. Up to this stage in the improvement of standards of living, more land is needed to satisfy appetite if the character and efficiency of food production remains the same.

As and when a person's income climbs well above the cost of a sufficient quantity of food, then he becomes more particular about the character of the foods eaten. Food of a carbohydrate type is cut down in the diet. Its place is taken by a greater quantity and variety of meat, milk products, fruit and green vegetables. In addition, there is more waste of food through heavier trimming of meat and vegetables and the throwing away of food left over from each meal. Meat and dairy products take relatively greater amounts of land to produce than do cereals and vegetables as a twofold process is involved. First, food has to be grown to feed the animal, such food involving crops like cereals, root and fodder crops, and grass leys. Then the animal has to convert this into flesh or milk, and in this conversion there is a considerable wastage of both food nutrients and bulk.

This trend whereby human food needs involve an expanding area of cultivated land can be expected to continue if standards of living of people throughout the world improve. Conversely, the constant work of the agricultural scientist is making it possible for more and better quality food to be produced from each acre of land.

But agriculture is only one, albeit the largest, of the many industries and interests which need land space. What is happening to the other land users? The chief uses in modern societies can be listed thus:

(1) Agricultural land
(2) Forest and woodland
(3) Recreational land—linked with the two previous uses and with nature reserves and water-gathering grounds
(4) Land for site purposes—inside and outside town areas
  (a) residential
  (b) manufacturing
  (c) commercial
  (d) transportation and communication
  (e) education
  (f) administration
  (g) defence
  (h) minerals

This list is roughly in order of area covered.[1]

[1] Ely, R. T., and Wehrwein, G. S., *Land Economics*, The Macmillan Company, New York, 1940, p. 5.

Agriculture is by far the largest user if the vast areas of ice, tundra, mountain, unexploited forest and desert, which man has left all but unused, are ignored. Even in a heavily industrial country such as Britain, land in farming use extends over more than four-fifths of the total area. Forest land is the next in relative importance, though its area, natural woodland and planted, varies tremendously between countries. In Brazil, for example, it covers nearly three-fifths of the total area of the country, in the United States of America about one-third and in the United Kingdom less than one-fifteenth.

The use of land for recreation is something which is quite new in character because of the recent deliberate allocation of relatively large and specific areas of land to satisfy such a demand. The need and desire for leisure is as old as the human race. As the machine has been developed to help mankind, and the production of material wealth has increased through specialisation and division of labour, it has become possible for larger numbers of people in society to have shorter working days and weeks. In order to use this greater amount of free time there are many hobbies which can be pursued indoors, and the modern developments of the radio and television are important in this connection. But with an increasing number of people being employed in office and industrial jobs, which involve indoor work and fairly sedentary occupations, it is likely that the desire for outside active recreation will grow. Within towns and close to home there are the valuable recreational outlets of the domestic garden, local sports fields, footpaths and public parks, and these local recreational needs are already accepted and planned for to a substantial degree.

As most people in the Western world live in large and small towns and cities, they are in an environment which tends to insulate them from both the vagaries and the realisation of nature. Moving from one lighted, heated and furnished building to another through a protected transport system, it is quite easy to forget that natural forces have much real importance. This has led to a strong demand by townspeople for more visual situations dominated by biological features—from the planned flower bed and mown grass of the city park to the ordered harmony of the stretches of farming countryside and the wildness of coastline, peak and mountain top. For a long time human society has been able to satisfy this rural urge of townspeople by allowing them to walk through and over the farmed countryside. But with larger numbers of people wanting to do this and better means of communication making it possible, society has had to begin to protect its rural land resources against too much indiscriminate multiple use. Areas of land are being set aside for recreational purposes with the conscious decision that a major use of the land will be for people to wander over and enjoy it, and that commercial uses, like timber production and crop or livestock farming, though continuing, will be secondary in emphasis.

Some countries, and the United States is one, are fortunate in that the competition between multiple uses is not so severe in the areas of rough land which people wish to use for recreation. Although many visit the American State and National Parks, these can be made large enough to accommodate millions of people and yet give to individuals a sense of isolation and being 'away from it all.' In more densely populated countries like Great Britain, Holland and Denmark, it is impossible to set aside large areas of rural land where recreational needs dominate completely. An uneasy peace therefore has to be imposed on a number of uses for certain attractive areas of rural land with, often, agriculture, forestry, water gathering and tourists all using the same area.

Land for site purposes covers all the paraphernalia that is necessary for man's physical convenience, from the site of his house to his roads and railways, shops and public squares, factories and mineral spoil heaps. Man has always used land lavishly for such purposes if he has been able to afford it. It is rather important for us to remember this or else we may delude ourselves into thinking that the spread of urban areas springs from a recent and new desire of mankind. The only recent change is the growth of wealth and its wider distribution which has enabled many persons and groups to secure possession and access to larger areas of land.

In most countries, either over most of their history or at least for long periods of it, social status has been associated with the control of land. For many persons control of land has been a dominant driving force, and the individual has often been content with his place in society if he has been able to secure wealth or status derived from the more extensive forms of land use like forestry and agriculture. Since the industrial revolution (which began during the eighteenth century in Britain and came later in most other countries), new and more valuable forms of wealth in land have become available to individuals. These have included areas for mineral exploitation, for factory development, or for commercial property. Often, the areas of land concerned have been small, being merely the sites of buildings, and even where they have been large the amenity value of the land has often been low.

No matter whether wealth is derived from extensive or intensive land uses the gratification of that wealth and the standard of living it brings and maintains usually involves a lavish *private* use of land. As the fortunes of individuals improve we see certain changes in their personal living habits. Starting, perhaps, in a tenement flat in a crowded part of a city they first move, on attaining a higher income, to a suburban house with a small garden. The next step from this may be to a detached house on a large plot in a 'better' part of the residential fringe. With some who become rich, there may be the eventual purchase of a small country property and, for a few, the large mansion with acres of grounds, lakes and orchard, a home farm and a few farms let off to tenants.

It was only for the fortunate few that the difficulties of distance and poor transport facilities during the centuries up to the twentieth were overcome by a combination of two residences—a country estate and a town house. In the twentieth century, however, the rising standards of living of ordinary men and women in many countries, aided by the motor vehicle, has meant that individuals can spend more on where and how they live. Thus, for the first time in history, many millions of people have been able, often with the help of sympathetic and supporting Governments, to do something about their own poor living accommodation—to move out of overcrowded rooms and tenements in the industrial centres of cities and away from poor small country cottages to more spacious accommodation in new flats and houses. Many have been able to achieve separate accommodation for families and separate rooms for individuals.

As more of such dreams become realities, it is obvious that the residential use of land will increase. As people find it easier to spread themselves more thinly on the ground and to separate their work places from where they live and from where they play, it is obvious that all other uses of land associated with towns will also increase. The motor-car, by itself, has been responsible for a considerable loosening of the residential pattern of many towns and cities, and this process is still continuing.

Modern industry and commerce, too, are physically so very different from the early days of the Industrial Revolution. Today, the single-storey factory building is typical, laid out with plenty of light in a spacious setting, with driveways, flower beds and parking lots. Going, or gone, are the multi-storey buildings packed tight against each other with machinery and people working on many floors. With the change of emphasis from rail travel to the use of road transport, the location of factories has also significantly changed. Although new factories handling bulk goods are still placed close to main railway lines or to branch ones, the spread of electricity and development of road haulage have enabled many smaller factories to be erected on the edge of towns and on the main roads to other centres.

Administration and the physical trappings necessary to it have increased with the complexity of modern civilisation and the larger number of people who are in service occupations and professions of all types. Here again the large blocks of offices in the centres of towns have increased in number and size but at the same time many new blocks are being situated where land is more easily and cheaply available. The one-storey office block has come into its own and in parts of our own administrative machine we are beginning to show the same lavish use of land as is occurring in so many other uses.

All such changes and trends in the uses required from land give rise to a situation where there is bound to be a degree of struggle and competition for land, more especially in the thickly populated countries. In addition, individuals are becoming more aware of how much land the other person has got. Easier, quicker and cheaper transport enables towns-folk to see the seeming plenty of land in the countryside, and the farmer to see what he conceives to be waste and lavishness in the city.

Without any form of land control or planning, the use to which a piece of land is put is finally decided by the price which is offered for it. In this circumstance, the use or interest which needs land in large amounts, because it uses it extensively, is bound to lose in the competition for land with other interests. Agriculture can, therefore, easily overpay for its land. Take, for example, the attitude that an industrialist, needing a new factory site, will have to the price of a suitable piece of land in contrast to a farmer. For instance, on a piece of land priced at £1,000, an industrialist may put a factory costing half a million pounds to build and producing a million pounds' worth of goods a year. The area of land involved may only be an acre or so. If a farmer has that acre he is unlikely to invest fixed and working capital in it above £100 and the output of ordinary agricultural crops and livestock is unlikely to be more than £100 a year. Quite obviously, the limit at which a farmer will be outpriced for land is quickly reached whereas what an industrialist is prepared to pay will be, though large, a very small pro-portion of the total capital involved in his project and an even smaller proportion of the annual turnover when the new factory is in production.

Some of the problems which arise because of this inten-sified competition for land will be dealt with in this book, with particular reference to those which occur between agriculture and other uses of land. We shall be discussing the interaction between the farm and the growing city, and though the problems will be discussed in general terms, the detailed evidence will be drawn mainly from experience gained in Great Britain. The first task is to show exactly how much land is being used for different purposes at the present time and to chart the major trends occurring in each use. We shall need to satisfy ourselves about the kind of land that is wanted for each use and from this discuss the effects of urban growth on agricultural production.

Many people may think that agriculture suffers from the growth of towns without any compensating advantages. This is not true. There is in fact a wide variety of advantages as well as disadvantages which it is important to think about and discuss. Yet if there is to be free competition for land between agriculture and, in particular, urban development, then agriculture, paying the lowest price, will always have to take what remains. If price is not allowed to be the sole arbiter of the use to which a piece of land is to be put we are confronted with the problem of effectively planning land use. These problems are particularly difficult in a democracy and in any country where there are many uses and a limited amount of land. It is hoped to demonstrate methods whereby the real strength and weaknesses of any particular demand for land can be worked out so that the community can make more rational judgments. If any society decides that it is not going to allow decisions on land use to be made by market price only, it is surely necessary to evolve other methods of comparison.

Finally, much more attention needs to be given to the constructive side of rural/urban land competition. There can be too much worrying about the difficulties and dangers of losing large areas of agricultural land to non-agricultural purposes. This occurs when the argument is left on a defensive basis and when the community does not, at the same time, check that good use is being made of the remainder of its rural land. In most areas and in most countries there is land now uncultivated which could at a cost be brought into agricultural cultivation. In Britain, for example, there are some coastal areas which could be reclaimed, many pieces of derelict woodlands and waste ground in the lowlands, and large stretches of unenclosed and unimproved mountain land in the west and north of the country.

How does a democratic community decide when and

where it is worth while to reclaim or bring in some or all of this land? Is it more worth while to intensify the use of the land already in agricultural use rather than attempt to extend the agricultural area by using scarce capital and other resources on such a task? When the pressures from non-agricultural uses increase in a country, it behoves that country to look more and more carefully and critically at its remaining areas of rural land and to work out techniques for measuring and deciding what is worth doing with that land. It will be shown in later chapters that some of the policies of land saving and land improvement existing at the present time in Britain have been conceived, and are being implemented, in isolation. This means that, as a community, we are investing too much of our resources in the use of certain areas of land whereas on others we are spending too little. All in all, we have not yet resolved the basic problem of how to use or improve our land in the most economical and worth-while fashion.

Chapter 2 The Measurement of Land Uses

THE area and uses of land in a country and the numbers of its people are fundamental to the character of its development. They are so important in relation to the production and distribution of wealth that it would be thought that most countries would measure accurately what they have available in these resources and how the use of them is changing. Yet, in Britain, knowledge of the numbers, scatter and occupation of its people is very much more complete than knowledge of the use of its land surface.

Some simple questions about land are therefore difficult to answer. How much land is available for all the main purposes of civilised existence? How is the surface of the country divided up between them? What changes have taken place in this pattern? What is likely to be the position in the near future? These questions are largely factual but are fundamental to rational decisions by a modern community in relation to the use of its land. Yet our knowledge of these things is, for the most part, vague and incoherent and there is no generally accepted statement concerning the national land-use pattern of Britain. Without accurate information the question of what is actually happening becomes merely the subject of considerable and indeterminate debate. It is, therefore, important to review the information existing on land uses in this country and to try to assess the defects or soundness of the major land-use records.

There are two broad reasons why our knowledge of how Britain is using its land is poor. The first arises from the fact that the land-use pattern is very complex because of the exceptionally varied landscape. To delineate, measure and then apportion each piece of land to its appropriate use, so that aggregate acreages under each heading can be known, is a prodigious task even though Great Britain is small in total area. A fine attempt to do this was made in the 1930's by the Land Utilisation Survey,[1] but, of necessity, the work had to be extended over a space of several years, and the face of the countryside was changing quite quickly while it was being done.

The second reason is that no one authority has been charged with the duty of measuring and recording how the land surface is being used. The total picture can only be obtained by looking at records made by different authorities interested in one or a few uses of land. Some authorities are interested in land use alone, others collect land-use data only as a by-product of other information which they feel to be more important. There are, therefore, no figures collected on the same basis for every use in the country. The chief sources of information from which our understanding of Britain's land-use pattern has to be derived are individual sets of statistics only. But the use of such records, which are not designed to harmonise with each other and have different ultimate purposes, must involve a large degree of incompatibility and overlapping. The whole field has been subject to so much doubt and confusion that at Wye College we have had to spend much time over recent years attempting to get order out of relative chaos so that a land-use picture could be produced which could also be checked and justified as reasonably correct.[2]

The records available can be discussed under the general headings of agriculture, woodland, urban development and residual or land not accounted for. First of all, however, we must decide what these terms mean in practice. In a country such as Britain, a satisfactory definition for land in agriculture is provided by defining it as 'all land used for the growing of livestock and crop products on a commercial scale.' This covers the intensive arable fields of East Anglia and the rocky unfenced mountain slopes of Wales and Scotland. It omits the areas of land taken up by the private garden and urban allotment.

[1] Stamp, L. D., *The Land of Britain—Its Use and Misuse*, Longmans, second edition, 1950.
[2] Best, R. H., 'An Evaluation of British Land-Use Statistics,' *The Chartered Surveyor*, 90, June 1958, pp. 660–3.

The 'urban area' is very much more difficult to define and the most useful definition is a wide one.[1] This includes within the urban category those non-agricultural uses of land associated intimately with cities and towns; things like houses, factories, public buildings, shops, parks, schools, roads, railways and cemeteries. It also covers the villages, hamlets and isolated houses in the countryside and the large area occupied by the road and railway systems in rural areas. The greater part of the multiple and special uses of land, such as opencast mineral workings, airfields and service training areas, which have rural as well as urban attributes, are, however, excluded.

But what of the uses of an urban character which also have a potential value for food production? Here we are thinking of private and public gardens, allotments, playing fields, certain golf courses, and so forth. It is important to classify these as part of the urban acreage. The main aim of these uses, after all, is to provide space, pleasure and opportunity for recreation for town dwellers, and as such, they are an integral part of the built-up areas by which they are, in fact, largely engulfed. The little plots of land used as gardens and allotments, though producing a share of the nation's food supply, are really not part of the agricultural acreage. They are invariably owned by persons whose occupations are more or less closely connected with the town or city in which they live or with some distinct non-agricultural employment. Such flowers, fruit and vegetables which they may grow are produced as a hobby and usually on a non-commercial basis for personal or, at least, restricted consumption. Moreover, the output from this type of land, though in the aggregate substantial, is highly variable, and it cannot readily be estimated as no agricultural returns are required from occupiers of land of less than one acre in extent. It seems impractical, therefore, to include such land in the non-urban categories, even though the produce from it supplements the national food supply.[2]

[1] Best, R. H., 'The Urban Area of Great Britain—An Estimate of the Extent of Urban Land in 1950,' *The Town Planning Review*, 28, October 1957, pp. 191–208.
[2] We shall return to discuss the food output of such gardens in Chapter 7.

Let us look a little more closely at the residue of land which is left when the aggregate acreage of agricultural land, woodland and urban development is deducted from the total land area of the country. This residue, or land which is not accounted for in our land-use records, contains some important uses and categories of land. For example, it includes rural land which is waste in a natural or semi-natural state. Even in a country such as Britain with a highly utilised land surface, there are unused areas of salt marsh around the coast and some stretches of fen, bog, swamp and mountain land which remain relatively untouched. There must, however, be very few parts of Britain that still possess an ecological association unmodified by the hand of man.

Much of this residue of land takes the form of dual or multiple uses which have not been recorded under other categories. A large section may well be taken up by land used primarily for defence purposes. Barracks and airfields, particularly the buildings and concrete parts, obviously have no other main use, but the grass area of aerodromes, and the large training areas and gun ranges on the hills are, in practice, only partially used for military purposes. Farming, to either a full or limited extent, does go on. Tons of dried grass, for example, are made from the short grass of aerodromes and hundreds of sheep wander across and feed with seemingly charmed lives on the no-man's land of artillery ranges.

In this residual group, too, must come other rural land which has escaped enumeration under the other major categories. For example, it is not necessary for occupiers of agricultural land under one acre in total to complete the returns asked for by the Ministry of Agriculture, Fisheries and Food. Similarly, areas of woodland of under one acre are not included in the woodland statistics of the Forestry Commission. Again, the opencast working of minerals is becoming a common feature of the British countryside as modern techniques make this method of winning minerals more economical than underground mining. Something like 100,000 acres will be used in this way between 1950 and

1970. Yet most of this land is only in this opencast use for a relatively short time. When the mineral is taken out, the top soil and sub-soil, can be, and are, placed back in their correct order. The land is then level graded, drained and returned to its former use, which is usually agricultural. The fertility of this land may well be different from what it was before the excavators began, but the former use is by no means lost. In the social accounting of land uses in the countryside, therefore, it would be wrong to place land worked for opencast minerals in the same category as the more permanent change of use from agriculture to a housing estate or to a factory building. The life of houses may well be over a century mark and even though urban buildings decay and are eventually pulled down it is very rarely that the land passes back from an urban use to the original agricultural one.

Records of agricultural land use

The main record of this use is the individual return filled in by those occupying agricultural holdings. Each year the area under crops, grass and rough grazings in England and Wales is compiled by the Ministry of Agriculture, Fisheries and Food from returns made by farmers on June 4th. This involves the analysis, in England and Wales, of approximately 380,000 separate returns filled in by individual occupiers of agricultural holdings of more than one acre in extent. The summarised results are published annually in the Agricultural Statistics. Information which is broadly similar in character is obtained for Scotland from returns collected by the Department of Agriculture in Edinburgh.[1]

The return made by individual farmers each June is made up of ninety headings for individual crops and grass, bare fallow, vegetables and flowers and fruit. Areas, which include field hedges, ditches and headlands, are recorded to the nearest quarter of an acre. Holders of land are required to record 'All land used for growing food or feed for any

[1] Ministry of Agriculture, Fisheries and Food *et al.*, 'Agricultural Statistics —United Kingdom Agricultural Censuses and Production,' H.M.S.O.

livestock (including grazing land) as well as flowers and nursery stock for sale, and crops such as hops and flax.' Occupiers are specifically asked to omit certain land uses from these returns such as 'private flower gardens, shrubberies, lawns, woodlands, osiers and willows and land under buildings, roads, yards, ponds, quarries and the like.'

Holders of agricultural land are required by statute to make these returns. It is clear at the outset that there is no statutory power to allow the collection of data on the *total* area covered by each holding. The only areas which have to be reported are the fields actually used for growing agricultural and horticultural products, together with the area under bare fallow.

Common rough grazings are not returned by individuals but they are calculated periodically for each parish of England and Wales by local officers of the Ministry of Agriculture, Fisheries and Food. As there is often considerable doubt as to what land is held in common and what is actually in sole occupation, these estimates must be treated with much reserve.

The collection of these agricultural returns, which record what the nation is doing with four-fifths of its land surface, began in 1866, but it was not for some years that the machinery of collection and recording was sufficiently accurate to achieve a reasonable standard of reliability. Furthermore, rough grazings were not added to the returns until 1891, and it was not until a year later that the minimum size of holding from which records were required became fixed at over one acre.[1]

There have also been changes as to whether a return made by occupiers of agricultural land should be voluntary or compulsory. The collection of the returns was on a voluntary basis until 1926, with the exception of the period 1918 to 1921, so that where certain occupiers on the parish list did not make returns estimates had to be made. But even the compulsory submission of returns after 1926 did not ensure anything like a complete enumeration of holdings. It is

[1] Coppock, J. T., 'The Statistical Assessment of British Agriculture,' *Agricultural History Review*, 4, 1956, pp. 4–21 and 66–79.

only legally necessary to make a return if one is actually asked to do so, and experiences during World War II, together with the earlier work of the Land Utilisation Survey, confirmed the suspicion that much agricultural land had been escaping the statistical net because the holdings in question were somehow or other not listed as holdings 'officially' deemed to be in existence.

It was in fact the exigencies of the 1939–45 war which really tightened up the accuracy of the Agricultural Statistics. New checks and regulations showed that there had been grave omissions in the basic returns. For example, rationing of feeding stuffs for animals was introduced in 1941, and it was then that many persons not formerly making agricultural returns found it desirable, in order to secure rations, to draw the attention of the Ministry of Agriculture and Fisheries to the omission of their names from the official records. The result of this indirect pressure alone was to bring in some 250,000 acres of land in England and Wales which had previously escaped enumeration. This meant that the total amount of land recorded as being in agricultural use during this time, showed a sharp increase, but this increase represented no real gain.

Similar, but smaller, additions to the area of land enumerated as being in agricultural use occurred in other years of World War II and subsequently. These were brought in during the closer examination of holdings by County Agricultural Committees in connection with various schemes of rationing, subsidy and grant payments and the more accurate map survey work of the war-time National Farm Survey. It can, therefore, be said at this point that the statistics of agricultural land in Great Britain have never been so complete as they are at the present time.

In all fairness it must be pointed out that the chief object of these agricultural returns is to assess the crop and livestock production of the country. Their value as a record of the actual area under agricultural use is only a secondary consideration. The important thing to remember, however, is that, although the return may be satisfactory as an estimate of production, the errors which remain in it may still be serious in land-use planning since it is the only available record of rural land use.

Problems of recording also arise in internal changes within agricultural land use. It is easier to record certain uses more accurately than others. This can best be explained by trying to follow the likely thought processes of a farmer as he fills up a June agricultural return for his holding. He knows often only roughly the total acreage of his farm. In practice, the natural thing for him to do is to take the total acreage of the farm as it was reported last year. He realises that if his total acreage is not substantially the same as previously reported there will be subsequent inquiries as to why his return does not tally with previous years. This type of influence tends to maintain a rigidity in estimates of total farm areas which may well hide some short-term changes.

The farmer is also asked on the form to deduct from the area of the farm any land that is not used for commercial food production. This is the area under roads, yards, buildings, ponds and so forth. These are quite difficult to measure and normally the farmer enters the figure which has been used previously for such residues. Thus, if a grass roadway is ploughed or a new farm building added, the tendency is to neglect the area they cover in the agricultural return.

Next, most people deal with a record form by starting at the beginning and moving through to the end. It is at the beginning of the June 4th return that the easiest things to measure are requested. These are the acreages of cultivated crops on the arable land of the farm. These crops are usually in special fields, the acreages of which are known by the farmer. He has had to make previous estimates of the acreages to be ploughed and cultivated in order to buy the correct quantity of different types of seed and fertiliser. The natural thing, therefore, is to insert on the form the acreages ploughed and sown.

In general, therefore, the area of land actually sown is recorded as the area under tillage crops. This area is not the same as the acreage of the fields actually planted with these crops because it often excludes the headlands and edges

B

which are unsown. These fringes are a considerable additional area because, in the field structure of southern England one acre of additional land is involved in headlands, roadways, hedgerows and ditches for every nine acres sown to a crop.

The remaining areas of land on the farm are the acreages under permanent grass and in rough grazings. There is little or no rough grazing on most lowland farms in this country so that the remainder of the farm, with the exception of the land under buildings, yard and roadways (and the temporary grass leys which are classified as arable) will be in permanent grass. In early June, at the time when the record is made up, the farmer is certain which fields he will be mowing for hay, and he can easily put this acreage in its appropriate column on the return. In order to get at the figure for the area of permanent grass used for grazing, the simplest method is to deduct from the total area of the farm the area under buildings, and then further deduct the areas under tillage crops, the temporary grass leys, and the area to be mown for hay. The remainder can be recorded as the area under permanent grass for grazing. This is the simplest way of calculating it, and by using a residual figure it means that the recorded acreages must add up to the area of the whole farm.

As a land-use record considerable error can come into the return when it is compiled in this way and it is likely to be hidden within this category of permanent grass used for grazing. It can, and often does, include discrepancies in the total area of the holding, the unplanted parts of the tillage acreage, and any errors arising from poor measurement of the non-cropped area of the farm. The latter arise quite easily because of the difficulties of measuring areas of buildings, roadways and odd pieces of woodland and waste ground.

In the rougher, poorer parts of the countryside and on the edges of the hills and uplands, farms do have considerable areas of rough grazings. In the agricultural returns from such farms errors tend to occur not so much in the areas of permanent grass for grazing as in the areas of rough grazing. There are some peculiar difficulties of measurement. The farmer may have common grazing rights on part of the rough land, or the land may be open or badly fenced. It is unlikely that frequent checks are made of its total acreage because the knowledge of its exact acreage is seldom needed for any farming operations such as seed sowing or exact fertiliser dressing. The acreage figures of land shown as rough grazing in the deeds of the farm, therefore, tend to remain unaltered.

There is also a kind of no-man's land between the edge of the poorer permanent grass in enclosed meadows in such broken country and the area of rough grazings proper, whether fenced or unfenced. The margin of cultivation is, in practice, a fluctuating line. Various factors decide at different points in time as to whether the enclosed fields are properly cropped or allowed to form part of rough grazings. The most important of these factors is the relative prices and costs of agricultural products. When agriculture and, in particular, livestock production is relatively prosperous, the limit of the enclosed fields moves slightly upwards on the valley slopes, the invading bracken is pushed back and even odd pieces of new land are reclaimed from the open rough grazings and put down to improved pastures. When the price levels of livestock are relatively poor, the rough grazings and bracken creep downwards to invade the top fringe of enclosed fields. Some of the enclosed fields would then be more accurately recorded as rough grazings instead of permanent grass.

Such peculiarities and errors in the original agricultural returns from both lowland and hill farms are particularly significant as these returns are used to measure changes in the total area of agricultural land in the country. The area lost or gained by agriculture in the course of a year in England and Wales is calculated by the Ministry of Agriculture, Fisheries and Food, from these June Agricultural Returns and, on each of these return forms, special provision is made for the recording of alterations in the acreage and occupancy of individual holdings. As far as possible the reasons for these changes in farm size are ascertained by the District Officers of the County Agricultural Executive

Committee, and the results are then summarised by the Ministry under six or seven headings to show the land uses to or from which the agricultural area is losing or gaining land. When as many as 80,000 holdings, or about one-fifth of the total in the country, show changes in area or identity each year, it is clearly often beyond the capacity of local officers of the Ministry to follow up completely each individual change without causing a long delay in the annual compilation of the Agricultural Statistics. As a consequence it is obvious that some land must escape enumeration for a time until the new occupier is called upon to make a return.

But the most serious difficulty arises from the fact that until fairly recently, a substantial area of agricultural land has been unrecorded as such by the Ministry of Agriculture, Fisheries and Food. When, especially during the 1939–45 war, land eventually found its way into the agricultural returns, the result was to mask the actual losses of farm land that did occur over that period to other uses. In the year 1941 the addition to the statistical total of land not previously enumerated, though actually in agricultural use, was so great that it converted what was probably an actual net loss of farm land into an apparent gain.

These remarks are not intended to imply that the Agricultural Statistics of this country are more liable to error or are collected with less care than figures for other land uses. In fact, until comparatively recently, they were the only comprehensive and regularly collected body of information available about land use in this country. It is, of course, the very fact that they have increased progressively in accuracy that has in some ways caused incompatibilities to arise in the data. It must always be remembered, however, that a small proportionate error in the records of a land use which accounts for more than four-fifths of the country's land area will, relative to the remaining uses, represent quite a considerable acreage of land. This is an important reason for exercising caution in using the Agricultural Statistics of this country as a land-use record. And because they purport to measure the largest major land use in the country it is useful to anticipate errors in the records of agricultural land rather than in the total of other land uses which cover a much smaller proportion of the nation's land surface.

From time to time special surveys of the agriculture of this country have concentrated on the land-use situation at a particular point in history. Examples of these investigations are the National Farm Surveys made during World War II in England, Wales and Scotland[1] and the post-war Types of Farming Survey in Scotland.[2] Although these surveys were carefully carried out, they were not primarily designed to measure or to check land uses and, in practice, they have often drawn on the general and incomplete Agricultural Statistics for their land-use material. As a land-use record the same kind of basic criticism can also be fairly applied to the Grassland Survey of England and Wales undertaken by the staff of the Welsh Plant Breeding Station under the direction of Sir George Stapledon just prior to the last war.[3] The principal object of that investigation was to produce a map showing the zonal distribution of different grassland formations but, in addition, the authors estimated the acreage belonging to each of the major categories of permanent grassland and/or rough grazing. These latter estimates were obtained by applying the results of their detailed field-to-field surveys to the total area of permanent grass and rough grazings given in the Agricultural Statistics. This means, of course, that the acreages obtained are based on figures whose limitations have already been discussed.

Records of woodland use

The contrast between the records of land used for forest purposes and those for agriculture is that whereas in the latter there is an imperfect but annual land register, censuses of areas under woodland have been made at more infrequent intervals. The first estimates which covered the period from 1871 to 1913–14 applied to woodland areas down to one

[1] Ministry of Agriculture, and Fisheries, 'National Farm Survey of England and Wales—A Summary Report,' H.M.S.O. 1946.

[2] Department of Agriculture for Scotland, 'Types of Farming in Scotland,' H.M.S.O. 1952.

[3] Davies, W., 'The Grassland Map of England and Wales—Explanatory Notes,' *Agriculture*, **48**, September 1941, pp. 112–21.

acre in extent. They were actually compiled by the Board of Agriculture from Statutory Returns made by woodland owners who filled in schedules distributed by local officers of the Board of Customs and Excise. In 1919 the Forestry Commission was set up and plans were made for a complete census of woodlands. The survey took place between 1921 and 1926 but the statistics were adjusted where necessary to make the census referable to the year of 1924. In 1938 the Forestry Commission initiated a new census, the results of which were to bear out the independent acreage estimates made by the Land Utilisation Survey between 1931 and 1938. In that census it was intended to measure, inspect and classify all woodlands exceeding 5 acres shown on the 6-inch Ordnance Survey Maps and also to carry out, simultaneously, a sample survey partly as a statistical check on various estimates made in the main census and partly to provide information about the area and contents of woods of less than 5 acres in extent. War broke out, however, before this survey could be completed, and during the war there was such a widespread felling of the existing area of woodlands that another complete survey was essential once hostilities had ended.

This was undertaken by the Forestry Commission between 1947 and 1949. All State forests and private woodlands of over 5 acres in extent were surveyed. In the interest of completeness an estimate was also made of the area of small woods of under 5 acres on the basis of a sample survey. This post-war Census was certainly the most accurate of all undertaken as advantage was taken of the experience gained from earlier surveys in its planning and execution.

Records of urban land use

Records of the areas under agricultural crops and woodland have been collected for so long a period of time in Great Britain that it must seem surprising that no really serious attempt to collect a comprehensive record of urban land uses was made until the implementation of the Town and Country Planning Act of 1947. One of the things that particularly distinguished this piece of planning legislation from its forerunners was that the proposals for urban development in any given area were to be preceded by a detailed survey of the area in question. Only then would actual planning begin. A further requirement was that in areas for which Town Maps were produced (that is, County Boroughs and certain town areas), a special land-use table should be included in the Development Plan. This would record the actual acreages under the various urban uses and certain other uses shown by notation, as outlined on accompanying 6-inch maps or 25-inch plans. In the table the details of these uses are divided into two columns which refer to the acreages existing at the time of preparation of the plan (usually around 1950) and those proposed for the end of the period of the Plan (normally around 1970).

These are the first statistics for urban land use to be required for planning purposes and collected together in a standardised form. Earlier planning legislation in this country was of a largely permissive character only, and the information provided was seldom in a form that has proved to be of more than local use. These early Town Planning Acts were concerned almost solely with proposals for forward planning and, although much lip-service was paid to the necessity for recording that which already existed, there was, in fact, little real action in this direction. Indeed, under the Housing and Town Planning Act of 1909, local authorities were only enabled to prepare schemes 'as respects any land which is in course of development or appears likely to be used for building purposes.'

It was, however, the Town and Country Planning Act of 1932 which provided by far the most notable addition to planning legislation prior to World War II. But here again the adoption of a planning scheme by local authorities was voluntary rather than obligatory even though it was now possible to include within the plan most, if not all, of the land in the area under their jurisdiction. The requirements of the 1932 Act in relation to land-use records were none-the-less still rudimentary. It is true that certain maps had, of course, to be produced in connection with the planning schemes. They had to delimit the area to which the schemes referred, indicate the land already built upon, and define certain land-use zones for residential, industrial and other urban purposes. But there was no necessity for presenting any detailed statement on land-use acreages derived from these maps, and even if this had been done the information would have referred broadly to the extent of land deemed necessary for new development and not to urban land use within already developed areas.

Even these figures, if made available, would have been of very little use, for one of the defects of the 1932 Act was that a paradoxical situation arose whereby rural land could only be 'saved' from urban development by zoning it for building purposes at extremely low densities of anything from 1 to 50 *acres* per house. Thus, by 1937, the utterly fantastic situation had been reached whereby the amount of land scheduled for housing in considerably less than half of the schemes actually being prepared at that time, was extensive enough, according to the Scott Report,'to accommodate a population of nearly 300,000,000 people additional to our present population of 41,000,000.'

By the end of 1941 only about 1,056,000 acres of land in England and Wales were covered by planning schemes that had been prepared and approved under the 1932 Act, although a further 26,000,000 acres out of a total of 37,339,000 acres in the two countries were covered by schemes in the course of preparation or which were awaiting final approval. It is quite clear, therefore, that any statistics that could be derived from these schemes must necessarily be of a somewhat fragmentary nature.

The most complete information on the extent of land under various urban uses prior to 1947 was not collected by planning authorities at all but by the Ordnance Survey and the Land Utilisation Survey. The Parish Area Book or Book of Reference of the Ordnance Survey, which was complementary to the original large-scale trigonometrical survey (1853–93) recorded land-use acreages, including urban land, under several headings. Unfortunately, this information was not summarised for the country as a whole and most of the original material was destroyed by enemy action during the last war. Between 1925 and 1952, during revision of the survey, 25-inch plans were also abstracted for urban and other uses, but records are very incomplete and again many were destroyed during the war. The only county for which records are complete and available is Middlesex which was revised between 1932 and 1935.

Land Utilisation Survey of Great Britain

This survey was the first and has been, to date, the only attempt to provide a completely factual record of the national land-use pattern by direct measurement. The idea was formulated by Professor L. Dudley Stamp, and carried out between 1931 and 1939, under the auspices of the London School of Economics, University of London. The object was to record on 6-inch Ordnance Survey maps the existing use of every piece of ground in the country. Some 22,000 separate field sheets were involved and the work of recording was carried out almost wholly by volunteers drawn from universities, colleges and schools. The completed maps were submitted to a general office for checking, editing and reduction to the scale of 1 inch to the mile before publication.

For the purpose of the survey, eight categories of land use were adopted. These were arable; permanent grass and meadow land; rough grazings, commons, heath and moor; forest and woods; orchards; nurseries; houses with gardens; and land agriculturally unproductive. The acreages under each of these divisions were measured from the 1-inch maps, using transparent one-tenth of an inch squared paper. The actual measurement of such areas on a 6-inch to the mile scale would have been too formidable and lengthy a task with the limited resources that were available. The results were recorded in the individual county reports which were published to explain and analyse the maps. The figures were brought together in a book written after the war by Professor Stamp.[1] This volume reviews and summarises the history, results and implications of this land utilisation survey.

[1] Stamp, L. D., *The Land of Britain—Its Use and Misuse*, Longmans, second edition, 1950.

It might be said that the survey had an agricultural or rural bias in that all but one of the categories of land use recorded were in some way related to food or timber production at a commercial or domestic level. All other uses were collected together under 'Land Agriculturally Unproductive.' This comment, however, does not detract from the survey's value in providing for the first time a directly measured figure for the urban land area at both county and national levels. This is obtained by adding together the figures under 'Houses with Gardens' and 'Land Agriculturally Unproductive.' Similarly, the approximate agricultural area may be obtained by adding together the five remaining uses after the forest and woodland area has also been taken out.

Certainly, the best picture of the use being made of Britain's land before World War II is obtained from this survey. It is now, however, more than twenty years old and during the time which has elapsed there have been fundamental changes in the pattern of home agriculture and a growth and change of character in the uses of land lying outside agriculture.

I T is possible to show changes in the more important land uses in this highly industrialised economy of Great Britain only as a progression of a few isolated pictures taken at different points in time during the first half of the twentieth century. In actual fact, the pattern of land use is changing in a smooth manner, rather than a jerky one, so that any assessment at a given moment is merely a snapshot of a continually changing scene. Because of the basic weaknesses in land-use records, however, it is only possible to produce a table of five different estimates between 1900 and 1950 in order to suggest trends in past and future land uses. Such measurements should be both more accurate and more frequent in the future as the Development Plans prepared under the 1947 Town and Country Planning Act are being revised from time to time. There should, therefore, be a number of new measurements and revised estimates between 1950 and 1970.

But the main trend of events in land use in England and Wales can be recognised from Table 2 and Figure 1. Since the beginning of the century there has been a progressive decline in the total *recorded* agricultural area from 31,050,000 acres in 1900 to 29,920,000 acres in 1950. At the same time there has been a persistent increase in the area covered by other major land uses. The woodland area has increased from about 1,900,000 acres in 1900 to 2,370,000 acres in 1950. The urban area and other forms of development such as opencast mineral workings and land for defence purposes have also shown rapid and extensive growth particularly since 1925.

It will be noticed from Table 2 that changes in the major uses have not been completely complementary. The decline in the recorded agricultural area has not been exactly matched by the increase in woodland and urban areas. It is necessary to take the column of 'unaccounted for uses' into account before there is a complete balance. Enough

Table 2

THE MAIN LAND USES OF ENGLAND AND WALES[1]

Year	Acres	Agriculture	Woodland	Urban development	Unaccounted for
1900	'000	31,050	1,900	2,000	2,180
	%	83·6	5·1	5·4	5·9
1925	'000	30,780	1,880	2,300	2,170
	%	82·9	5·1	6·2	5·8
1935	'000	30,380	2,120	2,800	1,830
	%	81·8	5·7	7·6	4·9
1939	'000	30,180	2,290	3,200	1,460
	%	81·3	6·2	8·6	3·9
1950	'000	29,920	2,370	3,600	1,240
	%	80·6	6·4	9·7	3·3

Total land area: 37,130,000 acres

has been said about the inadequacy of land-use records in this country to make the reader realise that the column of unrecorded uses is extremely important, and that it is movements in this total which explain the lack of balance between movements in the other uses.

The area in urban uses in England and Wales rose from 2,000,000 acres in 1900 to 3,600,000 in 1950, and it will probably be close to the 4,200,000 mark in 1970. Thus, whereas in 1900 about 6 acres in every 100 were taken up by urban uses we can expect this to be doubled by 1970. To bring the picture more closely in line with personal memory, it can be seen that between 1925 and 1950 the increase in the urban area was more than one-half. This emphasises how recent much of the growth of urban development is in this country.

Figure 2 shows what has happened and is likely to happen in a somewhat different way. When the rate of increase in the population of this country is plotted against the rate of increase in the area of land under urban uses, it is seen that whereas both increased at roughly the same rate up to 1925, since that time the urban area has moved sharply above

[1] Calculations made by R. H. Best, Wye College, University of London.

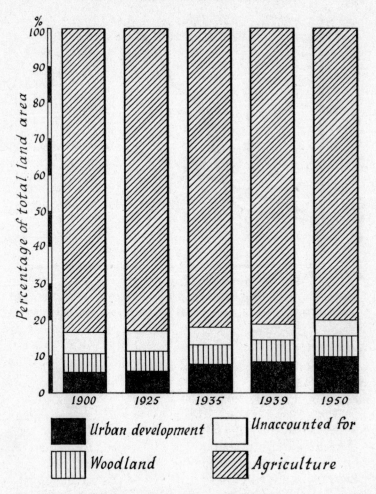

Figure 1: CHANGES IN LAND USE IN ENGLAND AND WALES BETWEEN 1900 AND 1950

population in its rate of increase. Though both appear to be levelling off, the urban area is likely to continue to climb faster than population. The important factor here, then, is the ever-increasing space standards demanded by human beings, and not simply the increase in their number.

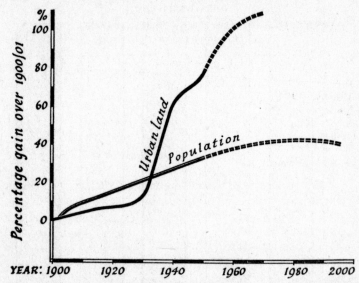

Figure 2: A COMPARISON OF THE RATES OF INCREASE IN
POPULATION AND URBAN LAND IN ENGLAND AND WALES

Urban land uses

What is the character of uses within this urban area? The
only detailed analysis that has been made of urban use has
dealt with the cities, municipal boroughs and large towns
for which Town Maps have been prepared by planning
authorities since the 1947 Town and Country Planning Act.

The proportionate composition of the total area under the
four main urban uses of housing, industry, open space and
education, is given in Table 3.[1] It will be seen that although
there is a broad similarity in the relative importance of each
use, the pattern does change as between the large metropolitan areas of Middlesex and London, the County Boroughs
and the large settlements.

If one attempts to weight the different types of urban area
by their population, the four main uses extend over 72 per
cent of the urban area, if small settlements and isolated

---

[1] Best, R. H., 'The Composition of the Urban Area in England and Wales,'
Journal of the Town Planning Institute, **44**, June 1958, pp. 160–4.

Table 3

THE USE OF LAND FOR URBAN PURPOSES IN SETTLEMENTS OF DIFFERENT SIZE AND TYPE

Urban category	Housing*	Industry	Open space	Education	Residue
	%	%	%	%	%
London	42·0	5·0	15·0	2·0	36·0
Middlesex	46·5	4·4	16·6	2·6	29·9
County Boroughs ..	43·4	8·1	18·7	2·8	27·0
Large Settlements ..	43·5	5·3	21·5	3·0	26·7

* Net residential area.

dwellings are excluded. The remaining 28 per cent comprises residual urban uses. Housing accounts for 42 per cent, open space for 20 per cent, industry for 7 per cent and education for the remaining 3 per cent.

As residential land accounts for more than four out of each ten urban acres in larger settlements, this means that houses with their backyards and gardens take up at least 1,500,000 acres of the total urban area if all categories of settlement and other urban land are included. Industry, on the other hand, occupies less than 7 per cent of the total and this represents less than 250,000 acres. It is surprising that open space represents such a high proportion and involves such a large acreage of land. It appears to cover one out of each five urban acres or nearly one-half of the area covered by houses in this country. It is salutary to realise that it is the second largest individual urban use of land. It appears that people in England and Wales live in houses (many with gardens) on 1,500,000 acres of land and use another 750,000 acres around them in their towns for additional recreation.

The relative importance of the four main uses also changes according to the size of settlement. In general, the area under houses and gardens becomes slightly more important as the size of the settlement is reduced. Industry, as a user of land, is relatively most important in the County Boroughs and large towns. The area under open space increases as the size of settlement becomes smaller.

The visual effect of the recently built schools with their

large playing fields is so dramatic that it might be thought that education is using a considerable area of our towns and land space. It can be seen from Table 3, however, that in no case is it above 3 per cent of the urban area. This means that our new schools and their playing fields are not likely to take up more than 60,000 acres in total.

There are obviously a number of important differences in the space used by people living in different ways and in different places. Out of the 50,000,000 people living in Great Britain, only about 3,000,000 live in isolated dwellings scattered through the countryside. The remainder live in small or large settlements. The occupiers of these isolated dwellings live at a very much more open density than those who live in settlements of any other kind. If the boundaries of their private homes and gardens are taken into account, each thousand of them occupy over two hundred acres in England and Wales (though considerably less in Scotland). This is practically double the amount of land taken up by each thousand of their neighbours who live in a settlement, whether it be large or small.

There is a great difference in the way in which settlements of different size straggle or huddle in the countryside. This is to be expected. The smaller the settlement the larger the amount of land it usually takes in relation to its population. For example, the people who are living in the villages and hamlets of lowland Britain are living at the relatively lavish density of 100 acres for each 1,000 persons as compared with only just over 20 acres for the same number of people in the middle of London. Anyone who believes that large areas of land under urban uses are a serious waste of land should be glad that most people allow themselves to be crowded together in cities and large towns rather than insisting on living in smaller villages and market towns. More than one-half of the population of England and Wales live in or near the fourteen chief urban centres, and yet this great concentration of people in relatively few cities or conurbations has been accompanied by a great economy in urban land use. If there were at any time a pronounced trend the other way, with people moving in large numbers to the smaller towns and villages, the urban area of this country could be expected to increase rapidly because of the relatively low density of people to land that is characteristic of smaller settlements.

The urban area of the future

What of increases in the spread of towns and cities in years to come? It is here that much argument has raged. Many people feel that little can be done to alter the extent of the existing areas of land which have already been urbanised, and it is therefore important to think carefully about the additional land which will or should be diverted to urban uses in the foreseeable future. This 'foreseeable' part of the future refers to a period of up to fifty years hence but most estimates have been concerned with the general period from 1950 to 1970 which is the period over which most plans have been prepared under the Town and Country Planning Act of 1947. Planning authorities have been asked to give in detail what they consider to be likely changes in land use for the first five years of this period with broader estimates as to what is likely to happen in the following fifteen.

Estimates of the likely increase in the urban area of this country have been important for two reasons. First, agricultural interests have become concerned about the area of farm land being used for non-agricultural purposes and they are particularly interested in any estimates of future demands. Secondly, it was not until after the 1947 Act and the estimates and plans of local planning authorities which became available in the early years of the 1950's, that actual measurement could be made of the urban area and likely future changes.

Some of the earliest estimates were those made by Professor L. Dudley Stamp.[1] Allowing for the rehousing of half the population of England and Wales at New Town standards, which were 53 acres per 1,000 population, he estimated that a further 2,000,000 to 2,250,000 acres of farm land would be required in the period 1950 to 1970 for housing, industry, open space, education, roads, mineral workings, reservoirs,

[1] Stamp, L. D., 'Planning and Agriculture,' *Journal of the Town Planning Institute*, **36**, March–April 1950, pp. 141–52.

the service departments and so on. This took account of the redevelopment of existing urban land. On another postulate, that of allowing for the rehousing of a third instead of a half of the total population, the figure was reduced to about 1,500,000 to 1,750,000 acres of new land. As a minimum requirement, which was an allowance for the rehousing of a quarter only of the population at New Town standards, and cutting down the allocation of land to certain of the other uses listed, Stamp suggested that an area of 713,000 acres would be needed.

This last estimate is very nearly the same as that computed by the Technical Staffs of the Ministries of Agriculture and Fisheries, and of Housing and Local Government in 1951. They accepted a total land requirement in the 'foreseeable' future of around 700,000 acres, comprising 500,000 acres for town growth, 100,000 acres for mineral working (allowing for some land restoration), 20,000 acres for new road works and the residue for other extensive new developments such as airfields and reservoirs. No allowance was made for land needed for defence purposes.[1]

More recently, the Ministry of Housing and Local Government has made another estimate of the total additional land which is likely to be required for urban purposes between 1950 and 1970. The computation, which is based on a sample of Development Plans submitted to that Ministry, gives a total requirement of 475,000 acres with a margin of error of 50,000 acres either way.[2] The lowest estimate of urban land requirements that has been made comes from the Town and Country Planning Association.[3] Their figures were 357,000 acres in this period to 1970. This covers town growth only and it consequently does not include land needed for mineral working, airfields, road improvements and so on.

At Wye College, R. H. Best has looked carefully at all

[1] Wibberley, G. P., 'The Challenge of Rural Land Losses,' *Journal of the Royal Society of Arts*, **102**, July 1954, pp. 650–70.

[2] 'Estimating the Spread of Towns into the Country,' The *Manchester Guardian*, August 30, 1954.

[3] Statement by the Executive Committee of the Town and Country Planning Association, March 27, 1953.

these computations and their qualifications. From his own work of analysis with the larger sample of town Development Plans made available by the Ministry of Housing and Local Government, and by the carrying out of new surveys of the amount of land taken up by small settlements and by isolated dwellings, it appears that the area of new land likely to be involved in urban uses between 1950 and 1970 will be between a minimum of 500,000 acres and a maximum of 700,000 acres in England and Wales.[1]

Most of this land will be taken from agricultural uses. The Ministry of Housing and Local Government has calculated from a sample of thirty-six Development Plans for County Boroughs, what is likely to be the proportion of land that will be taken from different uses. For the four main uses, residential, industrial, open space and education, it appears that 85 of each 100 acres of additional land needed will have to come from agriculture, a further 10 per cent from other non-urban uses and the remainder from the residual urban uses. (The type of agricultural land taken and the effect of urban growth generally on agriculture will be discussed in some detail in Chapter 4.) In Scotland the additional land required is not likely to be drawn so heavily from the nation's stock of agricultural land. The English County Boroughs will take only 15 per cent of the new land they require from non-agricultural uses. This proportion rises to one-third, however, in the case of a study of a sample of Scottish Town Plans.

The decline in the agricultural area

At first sight, the reduction of only about 1,250,000 acres in fifty years in the area in full agricultural use, as shown by the yearly agricultural returns, looks surprisingly slight. This apparent small decline has been used as evidence to show that the urban acreage must be growing very slowly. Our research suggests, however, that the actual decline in farmed land in England and Wales during the past half-century has really been 1,000,000 acres more than this.

[1] Best, R. H., 'The Major Land Uses of Great Britain,' Studies in Rural Land Use, Report No. 4, Wye College, 1959.

We have already discussed some of the difficulties in measuring the real area of agricultural land by the only land-use records available—the returns filled in by people who occupy holdings above 1 acre in extent. Let us look once again at the methods whereby the area of agricultural land is measured and changes in its area documented. The calculations are made from the annual June 4th returns. These exclude common rough grazings. The returns make special provision for the recording of alterations in the acreages and occupancy of individual holdings. As far as possible the reasons for these changes are ascertained by District Officers of the Ministry of Agriculture, Fisheries and Food, and the results are summarised by the Ministry under several headings to show the land uses to which, or from which, the agricultural area is losing or gaining ground. But for one reason or another, as many as 80,000 holdings, or about one-fifth of the total show changes in area or identity each year. It is clearly beyond the capacity of these local officers of the Ministry to follow up completely every individual change without undue effort and delay.

The procedure used has been described in the following way:

When returns fail to arrive from any occupier on the list the local officer makes enquiries to see whether the land has changed hands and has ceased to be used for agricultural purposes. In the latter event the local officer is expected to do his best to ascertain how the land is to be used in future. Similar inquiries have to be made when the acreage returned by any occupier is reduced. By summarising the explanations obtained in this way, it is possible to arrive at some approximate indications of gross losses of agricultural land in the course of the year and the main reasons for those losses.[1]

Every year there are also gains to the agricultural area which must be set against these losses; for instance, derelict land may be reclaimed, intended building sites may be vacated and land may be returned to agricultural use by the service departments. Immediately before the 1939–45 war, these gains amounted to something like 10 per cent of

[1] Ministry of Agriculture, Fisheries and Food, 'Losses and Gains of Agricultural Land in England and Wales,' *Agriculture*, 56, August 1949, pp. 233–6.

the gross total of agricultural land lost to urban and other uses. It is even more difficult to keep track of these gains to the agricultural area than it is to follow up all the losses of farm land that occur and, as a consequence, land reverting to agriculture may often be back in agricultural use for a number of years before the occupier is asked to make a return of it. On the credit side of the balance sheet there is, therefore, an element of uncertainty about the amount of land reverting to agriculture in any particular year and also the use from which that land is being taken. In fact, no detailed records of the latter point were kept before 1939 because of the large amount of effort often necessary to track down the previous use of a piece of farm land newly returned. The general heading 'Previous use uncertain' has often had to suffice.

The proportion of land gained by agriculture and so described is considerable. It has already been mentioned in Chapter 2 that until fairly recently there was a substantial acreage of agricultural land which has been unrecorded by the Ministry. When, especially during World War II, such land eventually found its way into the agricultural returns, the result was to mask the actual losses of farm land that did occur over that period.

And this is not all. In addition to straightforward gains of farm land previously unrecorded it was also frequently found that the area of an agricultural holding had been incorrectly given, perhaps for many years. The eventual correction of this error results in an apparent gain or loss in the agricultural area without there being any real change. Many of these errors probably date from the days of the part-time crop reporters prior to 1947, but it is worth noting in this connection that in 1948–49 the correction of errors or duplications made a difference of 55,000 acres. Again, it has been discovered that many so-called losses to woodland use from agriculture did not in fact mean an alienation of land to afforestation but rather that in previous years the area in question had been wrongly incorporated in the agricultural area that was returned. Therefore, the so-called loss in such cases represented merely a rectification of this mistake.

For all these reasons the year to year changes in the total area recorded by the Ministry of Agriculture, Fisheries and Food must be taken only as a rough guide to the net annual loss of agricultural land in any given year. On occasion, it may even be misleading. This is particularly true in looking at what 'officially' happened just before, during, and just after World War II when there were large changes in the so-called 'gains' and 'losses' of agricultural land. Table 4 gives the probable net decreases in the agricultural area of England and Wales between 1927 and 1954.[1] This was a period of expansion in the urban area and a time of considerable variation in agricultural prosperity. It will be seen that over the whole period of 1927 to 1954 more than 1,500,000 acres are thought to have moved out of actual agricultural use. If this is expressed as an average it shows a movement downwards of just under 57,000 acres of land each year. The changes between the four sub-periods within the table are, however, quite different from the general

Table 4

NET DECREASES IN THE AGRICULTURAL AREA OF ENGLAND AND WALES TO NON-RURAL USES, 1927–54

Period	Total area lost	Average area per year lost to:			
		Building and general constructional development	Sports grounds	Service Depts. and miscellaneous	Total
	acres	acres	acres	acres	acres
1927/8–1933/4*	337,000	37,800	9,000	1,300	48,100
1934/5–1938/9*	378,200	50,000	10,600	15,000	75,600
1939/40–1944/5	673,100	15,200	−4,500	101,500	112,200
1945/6–1953/4	143,800	32,100	6,800	−22,900	16,000
1927/8–1953/4	1,532,100	33,200	5,500	18,000	56,700

* Assuming that 10 per cent of the gross loss was offset by land regained to agricultural use. Minus figures indicate net recoveries.

[1] Best, R. H., 'The Loss of Farm Land to other Uses in England and Wales,' *Town and Country Planning*, 26, November 1958, pp. 426–31.

average. The drain of land from agricultural use was certainly not steadily maintained each year. This is only to be expected in a span of nearly three decades which include within it many exceptional political and economic circumstances.

The first period, from 1927 to 1934, saw the early growth of the new suburbia, reflecting the adoption of the Tudor Walters density standard of some twelve houses to the acre in towns and eight houses an acre in rural areas. This was a considerably lower density of housing than had hitherto been thought acceptable and more land was required to house the same number of people. The same period also covered years of intense industrial depression when building development in all its forms was very much restricted. At the same time, agriculture was being hit by the depression. Land was going out of agricultural use and farmers were reducing the production and use of their own land. During this first period, on balance, the urban area began to expand with some rapidity at the rate of about 47,000 acres a year.

This trend was very much intensified between 1934 and 1939. Agriculture was very depressed and even by 1939 was only beginning to improve its position. Cheap building sites on open farm land, combined with a revival in the sector of the national economy concerned with manufacturing helped to stimulate almost a stampede from town to suburban living. Space and light, a garden of one's own, grounds for communal recreation and leisure, escape from the cramped and dreary towns to attractive English countryside—these, whether adequately achieved or not, were the dreams and requirements of a population which was still growing in size. The result was an increased demand for ever more extensive areas of land, and it was at this time that the loss of agricultural land to urban development assumed its greatest proportions. The actual yearly scale of loss was over 60,000 acres. The close of this period, with the growing threat of war, also saw the beginning of serious competition for agricultural land from a new source, the service departments.

As might be expected, the needs of the fighting services accounted for the greatest part of the loss of farm land during the war years of 1939 to 1945. Indeed, because of their enormous requirements, which approached 100,000 acres a year, the diminution of the agricultural area proceeded at a faster rate in this period than ever before. This was in spite of the severe curtailment of house building. A fair amount of other constructional development, including the building of new factories and industrial plants did, of course, take place. Against this, however, the necessity of producing more of our own food led to the temporary cultivation of land formerly used as sports grounds and, as we shall discuss subsequently, the proportion of domestic gardens turned over to food production also increased at this time. Within agriculture itself, although there was a tremendous food production drive, most of the increase in output was achieved by the more intensive use of land already in an extensive form of agriculture. It did not involve large amounts of reclamation. There were certain attempts at bringing land into use which had been completely out of production, both on the fringes of urban areas and in the hills and uplands. Examples were the reclamations on the South Downs in Sussex and the Dolfor Hills in Montgomeryshire. These areas were small in total although well publicised. In general, we emerged from the war in 1945 with 670,000 acres less of agricultural land than in 1939.

The post-war years from 1945 to 1954 saw a reversal of some of these war-time trends. The service departments had by 1954 restored to full agricultural use about 200,000 acres of the 600,000 acres they had taken for a long period during the war. Similarly, the temporarily cultivated sports grounds were largely reinstated to their former use. Building and constructional development in general, after being held back during the war, surged forward to make up lost leeway but building restrictions kept that movement in check except for the political drive towards the construction of Council houses. In this period the annual average area of land given over to new urban development was some 39,000 acres. It must be emphasised that this loss of farm land, although substantial, was very much smaller on average than that due to similar development in the pre-war years between 1927 and 1939. This must be said because there has been so much comment on the amount of land going for urban development in the early years of the 1950's.

The periods taken in Table 4 have broadly corresponded with fairly well-defined historical phases in this country's economic and social development. It is important to emphasise that changes in the extent of new urban development can easily be masked by choosing periods for statistical comparison which suit a preconceived idea. For example, one could suggest that there is a very heavy use of farm land for development, giving as evidence the average figure of change for the period 1927 to 1954 which was about 57,000 acres each year. This statistic masks the fact that in the early years of the 1950's the net loss sustained was much below this figure, being in fact only about 30,000 acres a year.

Much attention has been given to this diversion of agricultural land to urban purposes because it has been the main change in land use in the last fifty years in this country. There are other movements, however, which are even more important in terms of area in many countries and which are also significant in this country. One is the movement of agricultural land into non-urban uses. Afforestation is, of course, the most important and in many parts of the hill areas of Britain where the Forestry Commission has been looking for new land, there has been considerable agitation about the conflict between agricultural and forestry uses for the same areas. But the national conflict has not been heavily partisan for a number of reasons. The type of land being taken out of agricultural use by tree planting has mainly been land on the margin of cultivation. Rough grazings or small farms with poor, enclosed fields have most frequently been involved and, though creating difficult personal decisions for individual families, the movement has not seriously affected the stock of good agricultural land in the country. In the second place, the area of land involved up to the present has been relatively small as well as low in quality. It will be seen from Table 2 that in England and Wales the area under woodland has increased from only 1,900,000 acres in 1900 to 2,370,000 acres in 1950, and although the programme of the Forestry Commission for new planting is quite ambitious, the rate of that progress to date has been rather slow.

The General Picture

Our research suggests that, after making allowances for discrepancies in the agricultural records and for multiple land uses, the total agricultural area of England and Wales has fallen much more steeply than the figures given in Table 2 would lead one to believe. The actual loss of farm land to all other uses between 1900 and 1950 may well have been almost twice as great as the 1,130,000 acres suggested by the Agricultural Statistics, totalling, perhaps, as much as 2,250,000 acres. Of this total, the growth of the urban area has accounted for 1,600,000 acres, while the woodland area has taken another 450,000 acres or so. The remainder can be accounted for by the increase in the area of such mixed land uses as military training grounds, opencast mineral workings and so on, and particularly in those parts of such multiple-use areas which have passed out of agricultural use.

The loss of agricultural land to all other uses in the first half of this century has, then, been about 7 per cent of the total agricultural area of England and Wales. This has not all gone to urban development. In fact only some 5 per cent has passed to that use, the remaining 2 per cent being accounted for by increases in the non-urban and non-agricultural uses of rural land.

In the second half of this twentieth century the interchange between major land uses in Great Britain is likely to continue at an even faster pace than that which has already occurred. We can forecast only as far ahead as the year 1971 since most recent estimates are agreed that new urban development and special uses are likely to require between 500,000 and 700,000 acres. This land will be situated mainly in the lowlands. In the hills, though the gap between what is planned and what is realised in the country's afforestation is large (and difficulties in closing the gap are by no means over), recent experience suggests that in Great Britain as a whole new plantings will go ahead at a rate of about 50,000 acres a year. This acreage will, of course, involve land of very low agricultural output.

Cautious extrapolation of present-day trends suggests that by the year 2000 the area of agricultural crops and grass in England and Wales is likely to be less by about 15 to 20 per cent of its 1900 acreage, mainly because of urban demands. At the same time the bare sides and tops of the hills and uplands are likely to be clothed by trees to the extent of a further 10 to 15 per cent of the area of woodland in Great Britain at the turn of the twentieth century.

Chapter 4 The Physical Effects of Town Growth on Agriculture

As the size of towns and cities increase and as individual dwellings become more and more scattered across the countryside, there is a growth also in the emotional reaction of many people to this land change. This is particularly true in areas and countries where people are conscious that the total amount of land available to them is strictly limited. It is patently clear that Britain could not feed all her people without some drastic changes in land use and in the organisation of home food production. Here then is a basic reason for an emotional attitude to land and its conservation. It explains why so many British people are sensitive to anything which appears to reduce the area from which they now get food or could get food in a crisis.

The idea of a crisis is built on reality. All people of mature age in this country have had to live through the 1939–45 period when food was scarce, diets were monotonous and there was the constant threat of a successful blockade of food imports into this country. All people over fifty years of age have memories of food shortages in two such national emergencies—the two periods of war blockades and submarine menace of 1914–18 and 1939–45.

The emotional content of land-use competition in Great Britain has been heightened since 1945 because of the clash of two opposing Government policies. The building of new houses came to practically a full-stop at the beginning of World War II. At the end of that war building began again with a large backlog of unsatisfied demand for new houses, together with a large amount of repair and renovation work caused by war damage and the sheer passage of time. In addition, a large amount of slum clearance remained to be done in most cities and there was very strong political and social agitation for this work to be carried out. In order to do renovation and repair work and to start on slum clearance, it was first necessary to create new homes and new urban areas on fresh land outside the city centres so as to provide 'elbow room' within the cities to begin demolitions. This, together with the general demand for new housing, has led to pressure for large housing estates on the periphery of our towns, together with the creation of some new satellite towns.

The outward movement of the physical area of the towns has run counter to the agricultural trend of the time. During the World War of 1939 to 1945, a large increase in agricultural production was obtained not so much by the use of increased areas of land as by a better use of land which was officially in agricultural use before the war but which was only partially and badly used. The war period therefore involved taking up the slack in the area of crops and grass by the better use of the land which had been previously badly farmed. This process was practically complete by the end of World War II. The agricultural expansion programme had then reached the point where new land was wanted for agricultural use and existing farm land was at a relatively high state of productivity.

The two programmes of agricultural and urban expansion began, therefore, to clash in the years following 1945, with an intense competition developing for certain areas of land around towns that were eminently suitable both for low cost housing and for agricultural production. In addition, certain other developments brought this inherent contradiction into full public gaze and public comment. The imposition in 1945 of a 100 per cent development charge on land changing its use gave the owners of land with a low monetary value no incentive to sell it to higher value uses. A land planning mechanism had been set up which abandoned the use of market price as a yardstick and substituted for it the deliberations and verdict of local planning authorities and the planning appeal. With market price removed as the final arbiter of land-use change, the existing owners of rural land often became its greatest guardians and its loudest protagonists in resisting change.

In the remainder of this chapter it is intended to look critically at the nature of this urban demand for more rural land and to weigh up the advantages and disadvantages of extended towns in their effects on surrounding farm land. Although this is a subject which has received some attention in Britain, the general problem and the argument flowing from it should be pertinent to the problem of expanding towns and rapid urbanisation in many countries of the world.

Types of farm land being urbanised

We have already seen that in England and Wales an increase of about 600,000 acres in the urban area is anticipated during the period 1950 to 1970 and that this will increase the total urban area from some 3,600,000 acres to 4,200,000 acres, i.e. an increase of 16 per cent. Though the area under urban use was still only one acre in each ten in 1950, its rate of increase has been extremely rapid during the last half-century. Any use which increases by 80 per cent in fifty years is worthy of some consideration.

There is little that can be done to reverse past changes of land use, particularly in relation to a permanent change from agricultural to urban use. There are many minor changes taking place within the urban use of land. Houses change in type of layout and parts of towns change from residential to commercial but rarely is land that has been built on later cleared so that it can be used once again for agricultural purposes. Though many human settlements in the past have declined and eventually disappeared through economic and social causes with the land coming back into agricultural use, there have been very few cases in history where man has deliberately planned the extinction of an urban area and its change back to an agricultural use.

Most of the extra land that is being taken up by new urban growth is land now in full time agricultural use. What kind and quality of farm land is this? Development Plans in themselves provide no information on this question for England and Wales. The proposals for most of the major cities in relation to future land needs can, however, be assessed in relation to broad types of farming. Table 5 shows the types of farming involved and the output in such agricultural use now being obtained from the areas shown, on a large number of Town Maps, as likely to be used for new urban development. It can be seen that the types of farm land likely to be most seriously affected by urban expansion plans are dairy farms (and mixed farms with a substantial dairying side), cash crop arable farms, and market gardens. Other important types of farming such as livestock rearing, corn, sheep and dairying, mixed farming based on arable production, and corn and sheep farming are less likely to be touched by prospective town growth.

Table 5

TYPES OF FARMING LIKELY TO BE MOST AFFECTED BY URBAN DEVELOPMENT IN ENGLAND AND WALES

Farming type	Proportion of total urban demands in land 1950–70 %	Average agricultural output of this farming type in 1955–6		Proportion of total 'net' output lost	
		Gross	'Net'*	£	%
		£ per acre			
Mainly dairying	53	40	27	9,952,500	35
Market gardening and cash crop farming	17	115	102	12,384,300	43
Other types....	30	41	31	6,382,700	22
All types......	100	53	41	28,719,500	100

* This is the gross farm production minus the purchase of products produced on other farms (livestock, feeding stuffs and seeds).

This table has been constructed by relating the proposals for future development, as shown in the Town Maps for the major cities, to the types of farming occurring on the land so affected.

The average value in 1955–56 of the 'net' agricultural output of the land likely to be taken for urban growth was £41 per acre. This is more than one-half as high again as the average for all farms recorded in the Farm Management Survey during that year (£24 per acre). Over the twenty years between 1950 and 1970 it is likely that land with a present 'net' agricultural output of more than £28,000,000 will be changed to an urban use.

Of the types of farming affected by urban expansion plans it appears that milk production could be most seriously affected, with more than 200,000 acres being situated on farms wholly in dairying or in dairying supplemented by other enterprises. Next in importance are farms with mixed enterprises but a substantial dairying side. The acreages likely to be taken from arable and cash crop farms and particularly from market gardens will be quite small but the annual output of such land is well above that of the land now in dairying. This is because dairy farming, though such a predominant user of the land of rural Britain, is of a much lower order of intensity in terms of 'net' output per acre.

The position in Scotland is rather different from that in England and Wales. Of the new land required for urban expansion, nearly one-third is to be taken from non-agricultural uses in Scottish towns as compared with the lower proportion of 15 per cent in the County Boroughs of England and Wales. In a sample of Scottish town plans, of the 8,121 acres of farm land needed for general town expansion purposes, 3,952 acres were derived from Class B or medium quality farm land, and 3,554 acres from Class A or good quality land. The area of poor land to be used is relatively small. It appears, therefore, that new Scottish urban development, though it does not take quite such a high proportion of agricultural land as the rest of Great Britain, is in practice also taking the better than average quality farm land.

The old-established pattern of rural land use in lowland Britain comprises many fields and farms of varied size and shapes, hedge-rows with frequent isolated trees, the small copse and the village with its scattered collection of cottage, house and farmstead. It is this pattern which, in many places, is being markedly affected by urban expansion.

Aerofilm

Aerofilm

Many people prefer to leave the congestion of the inner and older parts of the cities for 'a house of one's own' in the more loosely developed suburbs and near the countryside. Edgware, London.

The wastage and deterioration of agricultural land around towns

The change over of agricultural land to urban purposes is not smooth or quick. The process begins either with an area of land being zoned for urban purposes in a Development Plan or by an application being made to the local planning authority for the use of a particular piece of land for something very different from its existing use. This could be, for example, the use of a field or a corner of a field for one or more private houses, or the scheduling of a piece of land for the building of a new factory. The occupier or owner may be unaware of the contemplated zoning until the draft Development Plan is published. Then it is possible for him to object and state the grounds for his objection by appearing at the local inquiry on the Plan.

If the Plan is confirmed by the Minister of Housing and Local Government, the owner or occupier is then concerned with his piece of land in relation to the implementation of the Plan. If the land is zoned for change in the first five years, and it lies contiguous to adjacent development, the owner or occupier may well start taking steps to protect himself against the coming change of use. Knowing that the land is soon to be taken, the occupier may begin to farm 'to quit.' This involves taking out of the land in annual crops as much or more than one puts in so that the unused residue of fertility is at a low point when the land is finally taken. Certainly the pressure is on the farmer to use the fields which are threatened for short-term cropping and to involve himself in a minimum of capital or long-term investment.

Delays in the development of sites which have been agreed for change from agricultural to urban uses are bound to give rise to land wastage. There is evidence that considerable areas of land on the outskirts of many towns and cities do lie idle for some time pending their development. A study of such areas in the county of Warwickshire was made between 1943 and 1956 by the Agricultural Land Service Research Group of the Ministry of Agriculture,

C

Fisheries and Food.[1] This survey involved all the sites to which agricultural clearance had been given for a change of use over this period. All sites were reviewed as at June 1956 in order to see whether they were in their new urban use, or still in their original agricultural use, or if the land had come out of agricultural production but was lying unused.

The survey covered 12,000 acres of land which had been scheduled during this period for urban and industrial development in Warwickshire. The results showed that there was a considerable lag in the development of agreed land-use changes. In fact, at the time of the survey less than two-thirds of the total area agreed by the Ministry of Agriculture for urban uses between July 1943 and June 1956 had actually been taken out of farming at the end of that period. More than one-third of the total area agreed for new uses was still being cropped or grazed. This continuation of its agricultural use varied widely, between a minimum of 22 per cent and a maximum of 68 per cent in respect of different individual local authorities. It was lower in the larger urban areas as compared with the rural districts. In addition, the nature of the agricultural production on this land and the standard of husbandry appeared to be much poorer in the larger urban areas than it was on land lying in or near the smaller towns.

About one-quarter of the land cleared for urban development was still lying idle at the time of inspection. Again, the proportion varied greatly between individual local authorities, but it was markedly higher in the large conurbation round Birmingham and Coventry. As might be expected, the smallest proportions of undeveloped land were found in the areas of the predominantly agricultural local authorities.

The survey showed that the average period for which the idle land had been out of production since its official agreement for a new use was about two and a half years. Although some idle land was observed under each of the major proposed urban uses, the amount of land wastage in terms of area and time was least with housing and greatest in the

[1] Agricultural Land Service, 'Warwickshire—A Study of the Loss of Agricultural Land for Urban Development,' Ministry of Agriculture, Fisheries and Food, Technical Report No. 4, 1958.

areas assigned for schools and their playing fields and for public open spaces of all kinds. The estimated average period for which land has been lying idle awaiting development was 2·1 years for housing, as compared with 2·6 for school sites and 2·9 years for open spaces. The evidence also suggested that, in recent years farm land 'cleared' for private as against local authority council housing remained for a longer period in agricultural use.

The reason for such time-lag and the waste of land associated with it arise from the mechanics of land-use change. Much of the land to which agreement was given for an exchange from agricultural use to a town use was involved in agreements covering large areas for housing estates to be developed by both local authorities and private enterprise. These housing estates usually also included provision for schools, open spaces and other amenities. Very often, the housing sections of such sites are completed well in advance of the other requirements with the result that blocks of land of various sizes, shapes and condition are left over to await their new use at some later date. Most of this land, being held for purposes other than housing, was either physically separated by the new houses from its original farmstead or was likely to be surrounded by urban development at an early date.

Land which is isolated is always difficult to farm. In addition to its separation from existing farm units, the area of unused land that is left is often small and of a difficult shape. It can also suffer from many or all such handicaps as trespass, theft of farm crops, lack of fencing and fixed equipment, severance, smoke pollution and weed infestation from neighbouring derelict sites. This problem is intensified in the large urban areas as compared with the rural districts, as the proportion of derelict land is highest in the former and the standard of agricultural production from the land continuing in agricultural use is not likely to be good. In isolated towns in rural districts the scale of urban development is smaller and people are usually much more sensitive to agricultural problems.

Though for various reasons, a certain amount of wastage

is unavoidable in changing over from agricultural to urban
land use, it is thought that the authorities responsible for
urban development should be able to improve the position
in many areas by adequate publication of their intentions in
regard to the staging of developments of the areas planned
for urban growth; by not asking for clearance a long time
ahead of the anticipated time of actual building operations,
and, finally, by trying to give some type of security to farmers
who use areas which are 'cleared' but are not required for
immediate urban use.

Another problem which arises in the spread of urban
areas is that each field or each acre are of different importance
in the farm's economy. Farms are like factories in that each
part is interdependent with the other. It is, therefore, possible
to put both a factory and a farm out of operation by seriously
interfering with an essential part of it. In a farm setting one
can realise the relative importance of different fields by
considering the vital pieces of land. There are, for example,
the night pastures, with a water supply, into which cows are
turned out after milking in the summer time; the field or
fields which have to be traversed in order to get to other parts
of the farm; the areas of dry, lighter land which can be used
for a combination of tillage and grass cropping on a farm
where the remainder of the land is heavy and wet. Agriculture
and urban development can only mesh smoothly into each
other if the nibbling from a farm by urban expansion is done
with due regard to farming processes.

Trespass, both of human beings and dogs, is always said
to be serious where the edge of a town abuts on commercial
farming though it is difficult to get unbiased and factual
evidence on this point. It is curious, however, that there
are many townspeople who would be horrified and indignant
at the use of factory workshops as playgrounds and interesting walks, who still do not see the farm and its reaction
to uninvited guests in the same light. The physical movements
of individuals can be regularised by careful marking out of
public footpaths, good fencing and adequate notices, especially if changes in the type of farming are being carried out.

The choice of farm enterprises on farms close to towns

does not appear to take place as the defensive reactions of farms to the encroaching towns but rather because of the advantages of improved situation close to an urban market. Thus, market-garden crops or vegetables on a field scale are often introduced, and dairy farming is prominent. In general, sheep farming disappears from farms which are on the fringe of major urban areas. The potential danger from dogs and the ease with which damaged fences can be broken through by sheep are sufficient scares to prevent the keeping of flocks of sheep on such farms. This is particularly true where a farm touches a part of a town which is taken up by houses at fairly high densities with little public open space. The fields which border such housing estates act as the playgrounds for the children who live nearby. In this type of situation the breaking down of fences and the damage to crops and stores such as stacks of hay and corn can be severe. But there is hardly any disruption of farming activities on land adjacent to the built-up areas of small settlements which have existed for a long time in the midst of farming countryside. The fields on the fringe are quite normally cropped and used according to the farming pattern of the area.

The physical effects of contact between agricultural areas and the edges of towns can, then, be quite bad or quite bearable, depending on the type of farming and the type of community. There will be trespass problems but these can be canalised to footpaths in one or two fringe fields without undue effect on crops or stock if the children and parents of the nearby houses can be educated as to the reasons behind normal farming activity. The situation is also improved if the urban development is at a reasonably low density so that gardens of fair size, open spaces and safe roadways are available to the people, and particularly to the children, who live there.

Urbanisation and agricultural development

Up to this point we have been discussing the local and physical impact of growing towns on agriculture. There are many other vital interactions between cities and farms of a social and economic nature and most of these have been very beneficial to human welfare.

The growth of urban areas, where it reflects the growing proportion of a nation's population engaged in non-agricultural employment, has been associated with increases in national wealth in which agriculture has also shared to a marked extent. Urbanisation increases specialisation of function both within the city and on the farm, and both city dweller and farmer have gained from this. Where the growth of cities reflects a major increase in the number of industrial jobs, the rise in total city income means a heavier expenditure by consumers. Some of this extra expenditure goes on food products, particularly on meats, dairy products, fruit and vegetables so that there is more income for farmers, whether they live close to the cities or further away.

There is an interdependence between city and farm in the provision of jobs which is very marked when it is viewed on a world scale, with examples being drawn from countries at different stages of urbanisation. Farms provide jobs for many people, not only on the actual task of food or raw material production but also in processing and in providing and maintaining services and transport to and between the farm and the city. Whereas in primitive agriculture and heavily agrarian societies, those who provide services to agriculture are few in number in comparison with the numbers they serve, in highly industrialised countries the relatively few farmers and farm workers have a large number of secondary people to service them. In the highly mechanised arable farming areas of East Anglia, for example, each person working directly in agriculture is serviced by another two people who may live close by or some distance away in a market town or industrial city.

The farm has for long been the provider of people as well as of food to the city. Producing too many people for its own industry to absorb, except in poverty, there has been pressure from within agriculture to export its surplus people. These, in some countries and in some phases of history, have had nowhere to go and so have stayed on the land, helping to depress the standard of living of rural people. In other countries and at other stages of historical development the surplus persons in agriculture have moved elsewhere to new land for agricultural settlement. But the main movement has been to the town and industrial city as new jobs and higher material standards of living have added a strong pull to the push of agricultural over-population.

In many ways a farm close to a thriving city is in the most favourable position possible—if it is able to keep its land intact. There are, of course, the physical disturbances of farming activities by town people if the farm is close to the town's edge. There is the increased competition for farm staff by the presence of alternative employment close by, but the scanty evidence on this matter, at least in Britain, does suggest that this competition is not entirely harmful. Certain studies[1] made of farming areas close to the growing town of Scunthorpe in Lincolnshire and the new towns of Crawley, Harlow and Stevenage, near London, showed that though there was a more rapid movement of farm workers to urban jobs, especially to construction work in the areas close to the growing towns, in contrast with farming areas further away, the level of wages was higher and farmers providing decent cottages and working conditions had little difficulty in replacing their men. The new farm workers came, usually, from village, small town or farm in more isolated parts of the country.

The farm close to a city usually benefits from many services provided in or by that city—better and more roads, railways, bus services, mains water and electricity, shopping facilities, entertainment, schools. The farmer can partake of these facilities and, to glance at advertisements in farming papers, he often stresses their presence and attractiveness when advertising for new workers. For long, too, the local town or city has provided the farm with the market for its products and has supplied all his non-food needs. This has been reflected in farming patterns, moving from more intensive production like field vegetables and dairy farming

[1] Agricultural Land Service Research Group, 'Planned Urban Development and its Effect on Agriculture,' *Journal of the Town Planning Institute*, **39**, September–October 1953, pp. 234–7.

through to grain growing and finally to livestock rearing as one moved away from the city and its influences and away from means of transportation.

The marked effects of these differences in location on farming patterns are becoming confused in some countries as continuous improvements in transport and storage, combined with assured markets and guaranteed minimum price levels for the major farm products, break down some of the barriers of isolation in rural areas. In fact, the preliminary studies of the impact of new towns on the surrounding rural areas showed no real change in the intensification of agricultural land use because of the presence of these new and growing urban areas. A change may occur as the population of the new towns rises closer to their final planned targets and time allows a better local adaptation of countryside to town.

Chapter 5 The Siting of Urban Development on Agricultural Land

Aᴺʸ modern community is faced with the problem of reconciling competing claims for the use of certain parts of its land surface. It is rare for any particular use to be completely rejected if it is accepted that the uses of land are socially rather than physically determined. The best use of any piece of land is therefore a relative rather than an absolute problem and we must accept that this best use can and will change from one generation to another, depending on the range and priority of uses that society wants satisfied from its physical environment.

The onus of proof

In weighing up a case for making a major change in the use of a particular piece of land there is a school of thought which believes that the use and users of the land in its existing state have a prior claim and that the proposed new use and new users should prove that the community will benefit if the land in question is passed over to them. This view is strongly held in relation to agricultural land in this country. The idea was formalised and argued by the majority of the Scott Committee which reported on land utilisation in rural areas in 1940.[1] In Chapter 13, para. 233, of this report, the case is put in these terms:

The Onus of Proof. Land which is included in one of the categories of good land should not be alienated from its present use unless it can be clearly shown that it is on balance in the national interest that the change should be made. The same applies when the question relates to land which, though of indifferent quality, may be an essential part of a well-balanced farming unit. We attach real importance to the *onus of proof*, whether a decision is being reached in a matter of wide national importance or in a purely local case. It is not merely that agriculture is in possession, actually or potentially, and that possession of itself puts the burden on the applicant who seeks to make the change, and, in the case of building, to bring to an end for ever the present form

[1] Ministry of Works and Planning, 'Report of the Committee on Land Utilisation in Rural Areas (Scott Report),' Cmd. 6378, H.M.S.O. 1942.

of utilisation. It is rather the method of approach to the problem. Where the land is of a good agricultural quality and there is no dominant reason why there should be constructional development, the task of the Authority is simple—its answer will be 'No!' But in the case of some of the intermediate qualities of land, especially where pros and cons are at all evenly balanced, or other sites are offered to the applicant as alternatives (and it is not easy to gauge their suitability in all such cases) it would be of very general assistance to all persons likely to want sites for construction, as well as to the owner of the agricultural land, and the Minister of Agriculture himself, if it were common knowledge that agricultural sites would not be handed over unless a clear case of a national advantage was made out.

In the paragraph which follows, the majority of the Scott Committee go on to emphasise their argument by saying: 'In any case we regard it as a matter of justice to the nation in any system for handing over agricultural land for development, that the applicant should be obliged to make out a good and clear case; in other words that the onus of proof rule should apply to all agricultural and forestal land.'

It is very significant that a majority of this committee should have come to the conclusion that agricultural land in Great Britain had a prior claim in the conflict of land uses. Their judgment arose as a result of taking evidence on land utilisation problems from a host of professional societies, institutions and individuals concerned with, or interested in, problems of rural Britain. The decision to elevate one use of land above all others in the matter of claim and proof is quite fundamental especially as that particular use of land covers more than four-fifths of the country's land surface.

The idea did not go unchallenged at that time. In fact, even within the Scott Committee itself quite fundamental disagreement arose on this point and this was cogently expressed in a minority report by Professor S. R. Dennison. At the beginning of his report he clashes with the opinion of the majority in relation to its basic assumption as to the maintenance of a prosperous agriculture in Britain after the end of World War II. The majority opinion rather assumed that this task involved a maintenance of war-time food output and a maintenance of the area of land being used for production at the time of reporting. Dennison emphasised that there could be an increasing output from an industry like agriculture together with a decline in the area of land it used or needed to use. As he was not prepared to accept the overall need for a maintenance of the agricultural area of Great Britain at any particular set level, it was quite obvious that he would disagree with the onus of proof argument of the majority which gave agriculture a prior claim to land. In Section 5 of his minority report[1] he lays out his argument, thus:

There are two specific objections to the 'onus of proof.' First I do not consider that it solves the problem. Even in the simplest case put forward, 'where the land is of a good agricultural quality and there is no dominant reason why there should be constructional development' (and the answer of the Central Planning Authority would be 'No') there is room for disagreement, according to the interpretation of what is a 'dominant reason' for construction. The task of the Central Planning Authority in giving its negative answer here is 'simple' only if it has general principles to determine what is a dominant reason. In the less 'simple' cases, and these would be the majority, there is nothing to fill this hiatus between the principle and its application. Nor will it be filled by the mere accumulation of 'detailed information almost everywhere as a result of research work' for the matter is not one of information of local conditions, but of differences of opinion about the relative importance of various imponderables.

Secondly, even without special machinery to protect agricultural land, it is a principle which might well prove highly restrictive; if rigidly applied, it could hinder many desirable town planning developments. The very fact that a 'developer' (whether private or public) is prepared to pay a price (usually much above the agricultural value) for a piece of land indicates an alternative use. If the use is for industry, then it is virtually certain that productivity will be greater than it is in agriculture; if it is for housing, or similar developments, then it is possible that there is a social need which should be met . . .

I consider it to be a primary national interest that such development should take place, and that nothing should unnecessarily stand in its way; it is particularly important that individual developments should not be held up on account of appeal to vague general interests. Thus, I am led to recommend the application, through the machinery of planning control, of a principle of onus of proof the reverse of that recommended by the Majority. It should be incumbent upon the agricultural occupier, or other agricultural interest, to show cause why land should not be diverted to some other use, and opportunity for

[1] 'Minority Report of Committee on Land Utilization in Rural Areas (Prof. S. R. Dennison)', page 119, para. 64.

such demonstration should always be provided. This would provide protection to the agricultural interest, possibly represented by the post-war successors of the County War Agricultural Executive Committees; for example, it could point to alternative sites on inferior land which might be equally suitable, and argue the case for the diversion of the development to such land. In this way, the best land would not be unnecessarily alienated from agriculture, while it would be a general advantage if it were common knowledge that constructional development would not be impeded by the maintenance of land for agriculture unless a clear case of national advantage were made out.

The quotations given from the majority and minority reports of the Scott Report have been ample and full because they deal with a fundamental conflict of views as to whether or not agriculture has any prior claim to land as against other users in a country such as Britain. The resolving of this conflict depends very greatly on the assessment of the country's economic position in relation to its total food supplies, and involves decisions as to what proportion and type of food would be better obtained from home land resources and which from land resources overseas through an exchange of manufactured products for food. In Chapter 6 evidence and arguments are presented as to Britain's present and future position in the economy of world trade and, in particular, in relation to the imports of foods of different types and her ability to pay for them. From this chapter and from later discussion of the problems and possibilities of intensification of agricultural production, it is clear that there is a good measure of support for the following simple conclusions.

(1) Though it is difficult to assess Britain's place in international trade in relation to food products, the combination of factors such as industrialisation in many other food exporting countries, problems of balance of payments and the stresses of economic and political warfare between the major competitive blocks of the world—all suggest that Britain can justify the *amount* of food it is producing on its home acres at the present time, though it must watch carefully that the cost of getting it is in relation to the costs of potential alternative supplies obtained from abroad through the sales of manufactured goods.

(2) The area of land in *effective* agricultural use should be considerably larger than it was before World War II.

(3) Within the 80 per cent of the land surface of Britain which is still in agricultural use there is sufficient room and facilities for producing the amount of food which it is in the economic and social interest of this country to produce from its own resources. This is because the loss of agricultural land to non-agricultural purposes is proceeding at a smaller rate than the increase in production per acre made possible by the use of improved techniques of growing and greater skill in management.

(4) There is unmistakable evidence (and some of it is apparent to the eye of travellers) that there are still considerable areas of agricultural land in England and Wales which are on a low plane of use. Many husbandry and economic surveys of farms continually emphasise the very great difference between farms in the intensity of the use made of land and other resources in food production.

It is difficult, therefore, to place the agricultural use of land on a higher plane of priority than other uses. But the movement of agricultural land to other non-food uses does involve local and national problems in land allocation. As agriculture still uses by far the greatest part of the land surface of most developed countries, new uses like building development have, superficially, large areas of farm land from which to choose. Where there are possible alternatives surely all societies should attempt to change to the new uses those parts of the agricultural area which can most easily be spared? This line of reasoning lies behind the emphasis on the use, wherever possible, of the poorest of any alternative sites of differing agricultural quality for urban development in Great Britain. The major difficulty arises from the fact that areas of agricultural land not only differ in their output, both actual and potential, of farm products, but also in the capital costs involved in their use for different purposes. It is important, therefore, to suggest a technique whereby a correct judgment can be made as to the relative importance of safeguarding the better agricultural land in relation to the extra costs involved in developing the poorer site. An

attempt is made to do this in this chapter and a description
is given of cases where the technique has been used.

How agricultural considerations are brought into existing town planning schemes

Before discussing a different method of evaluating the
agricultural aspects of alternative sites for urban development let us look at the existing procedure. Following the
publication of the Scott Report on the Utilisation of Land
in Rural Areas, the Uthwatt Report on Compensation and
Betterment, and the earlier Barlow Report on the Distribution
of the Industrial Population in Great Britain, the Ministry of
Town and Country Planning was set up in 1944 and comprehensive legislation arranged under the Town and Country
Planning Act of 1947 to secure 'the right and proper use of
land' in the country. In the setting up of County Borough
and County Planning Committees and in charging them with
the duty of preparing Development Plans for the most heavily
populated parts of their areas and for all counties in broad
outline, it was made incumbent on these authorities to take
into consideration any agricultural case in relation to any
piece of land where a major change in land use was contemplated. Again, early in World War II, a working arrangement
had been agreed between Government Departments that no
piece of land would be taken for non-agricultural use until
the observations of the Ministry of Agriculture had been
obtained.

The interesting thing in these arrangements was that the
concept of the 'onus of proof' being laid on the person who
wanted to change the use of agricultural land, as put forward in the majority recommendations of the Scott Committee, has not at any time been accepted or implemented.
In fact the type of approach suggested by Professor Dennison
in his minority report has in practice been a more accurate
description of what has occurred. Agricultural interests have
had to suggest alternative sites which were reasonably
suitable before their objection to the change of use of a
particular piece of farm land has been accepted by Planning
Authorities or Government Departments.

The existing procedure for handling land use cases is briefly this. Take the case of a builder who proposes to buy a field on which to erect a number of houses for sale or letting. His first task is to find a willing seller. This will be greatly influenced by whether or not the piece of land in which he is particularly interested has been allocated for ultimate residential use in the Development Plan of the area. If the field has been so allocated then the builder will know that if he can purchase the field he should have no difficulty in gaining general approval of the planning authorities. The owner of the land, on the other hand, can of course refuse to sell but he will be influenced towards selling, first, by the high price relative to its present agricultural value which he can ask and get, and, secondly, by the fact that as the land is zoned for residential development, it can in the last resort be compulsorily acquired from him, if the Local Authority becomes convinced that the lack of a willing seller is seriously prejudicing the right development of the area.

The way in which the agricultural case is handled depends on whether the field in question lies within or outside an area already scheduled for residential development under a Town Map. If it lies within that area, its agricultural value has been taken into account in the consideration of the whole town and the areas which could rightly be scheduled for urban development. Each Planning Committee asks the Ministry of Agriculture, Fisheries and Food, through its Agricultural Land Service, for an appreciation of the agricultural value and usefulness of the land around its main urban areas. From the survey information provided by that Ministry, it tries to choose the area with the least agricultural significance providing there are no overriding planning considerations.

The planning authorities make as careful an assessment as they can of the likely future demands for land of that community in the immediate five-year period and on a broader scale up to 1970. This analysis takes into account factors such as the present and likely future population numbers, surveys of the age and condition of buildings, assessment of housing needs (for new families and the provision of better homes for overcrowded areas), employment trends in local industries, provision and need of open spaces, the school building programme and necessary and desirable road improvements. The combined result of these analyses is that the local planning authority is able to say to the Ministry of Agriculture something like the following: 'For Town X we anticipate that an additional 500 acres of land will be needed between 1950 and 1970. We would like about two-thirds of this land to be available on the north side of the town, and the remainder on the south, and in relation to these areas, certain specific plots of land must be taken for urban development, no matter what quality agricultural land they are, because there are no other possible sites for the particular uses which must be made of them.'

The Ministry of Agriculture is, in practice, presented with a claim for land which is based on an analysis done by the staff of the local planning authority, with help from the planning personnel of the Ministry of Housing and Local Government. This claim is, however, often quite specific in detail stating, not only the rough amounts of land needed but approximately where they will have to be found. Therefore, the most that the Ministry of Agriculture can do is to make a relative grading of the land around the town and reply thus: 'For your 500 acres we suggest that you take the land marked brown on this map, and that, if possible, you stagger your development in the stages we suggest. These stages, if they can be complied with, will mean that the poorer farm land is taken before the better and that interference with farm units is kept to a minimum.'

Let us return to the field wanted by the builder. Its agricultural value will already have been assessed if it is within the area zoned for residential use on the Development Plan, and there will be no further general consideration of its agricultural importance. This situation is, in general, fair because, together with prior consultation with the Ministry of Agriculture, the Development Plan for the urban area, when it is first drawn up, is only in draft form and its form and content is available for public inspection and disagreement. The plan for any particular town or area is only approved by the Minister of Housing and Local Government after careful perusal and after taking into account any objections made by interested parties. These objections are considered at public local inquiries where anyone whose interests are affected by the proposed scheme is free to state his case before an inspector of the Ministry of Housing and Local Government. Therefore, agricultural interests really have two lines of defence—the general survey of the Ministry of Agriculture and the opportunity for individual argument at the public local inquiry on the Development Plan.

If the field in which our builder is interested lies outside the area zoned for residential development in the Town Map, or is in an area or attached to a community where no Town Map has been prepared the situation is somewhat different. The builder will usually make a contract with the seller that he will buy the land concerned for a certain price for certain purposes *IF* planning permission can be obtained for this change of use. He will then make application to the local planning committee for permission to build. If the field concerned is just outside an area for which a Town Map has already been prepared it is likely that the application will be turned down unless there are unusual reasons for it. In any case, lying as it does outside the designated area, it is probable that the opinion of the Ministry of Agriculture will be sought as to the agricultural value of the land concerned.

When the field concerned lies in an area where a Town Map has not been drawn up, the particular site is considered by the local planning authority on its merits. As part of the evidence needed in the discussion of planning problems created by its proposed change of use a report would be obtained from the Ministry of Agriculture. In both cases, that is, whether the site lies close to a Town Map area or well outside it, the decision of the planning authority on the particular site would be conveyed to the person making the application. It is then up to the applicant to appeal against the decision if he is unhappy about it. This appeal is to the Minister of Housing and Local Government and a public local inquiry is normally held.

It is important to remember that there is a very definite
procedure whereby private individuals who think that their
case has not been fairly judged can appeal and have the
case reconsidered by persons who are independent of those
who originally made the decision against them. This is, of
course, a democratic safeguard which applies to very many
fields of individual activity in this and many other countries.
In addition, the agricultural value of the land, both in a
broad and narrow sense, is considered at more than one
stage and there is a procedure whereby disagreement over
the agricultural value of the land can be pressed to a very
high level in the local and national administrative machinery
of the country. If agreement cannot be obtained between
the local representatives of the Ministry of Agriculture and
the Planning Committee, then the agricultural case is re-
argued by the headquarters of the Ministry of Agriculture
with the headquarters of the Ministry of Housing and Local
Government, through the particular case being 'called in'
by the latter Minister. In the last analysis, the final decision
on disputed cases is taken by the Cabinet. There have been
a number of cases, especially where unusually large quantities
of land were involved and where alternative sites have been
difficult to find or to be agreed, where a Cabinet ruling has
had to be made.

Weaknesses of the present method

Though there is a very definite procedure whereby the
agricultural value of the land in question is considered before
a final and irrevocable decision is made to change its use,
the basis of the assessment of the agricultural value of a
particular piece of land to the community in its present, as
against its proposed new use, is still quite unsatisfactory.
The only way in which a negative answer can be given to a
proposed change of use of a piece of agricultural land is if
there is another piece of land which can be used for the new
purpose with only a minimum of additional cost and inconvenience. But the difference in the value of the alternative
sites in their agricultural production may justify more than
a minimum of additional cost and inconvenience to building

operations. At the present time an argument between two sites of differing agricultural value and of differing costs of development is expressed in terms of differences in physical output on the farm side and in once and for all capital costs in relation to building construction.

This means that protagonists of different uses of land, like agriculturists and housebuilders, argue in different languages. Those concerned with urban development assess the land they want to use in terms of money costs of site works. An example of their type of evaluation might run thus: 'If Site B has to be used for house building instead of Site A it will cost £50 more per house because of additional clearance work or extra foundations.' Against this type of estimate in pounds sterling of extra costs are placed statements of another kind—of differences in gallons of milk per acre, in hundredweights of grain, in tons of potatoes or a certain number of cattle or sheep kept per acre on the two sites in their present agricultural use.

Combinations of such figures into crop yield indices or, more completely, into calories produced per acre still leave the relative agricultural valuation in different terms from the financial statements of those interested in building on either area of land. Attempts to measure *potential* agricultural production rather than present output of the land under question also leaves the answer in a form that is difficult to use or compare with site costs and other considerations.[1] In addition, extra money cost, to be incurred almost immediately by those building on the land, has to be compared with an agricultural revenue from the same piece of land which the community will only receive in relatively small annual amounts.

It is patently clear that a local planning committee or a planning inspector, trying to balance the alternative uses for a piece of agricultural land, will find it very difficult as the facts are in such different forms. Often, too, even mixed and incomplete facts like these are missing. Some local

[1] For example, the interesting calculations of Professor L. Dudley Stamp in relation to 'Potential Production Units'—see *The Under-Developed Lands of Britain*, Soil Association, London, 1954.

authorities, for example, although aware and appreciative of direct and sometimes indirect costs involved in developing a site, often do not go beyond a general statement such as 'Site B will be much more expensive to develop than Site A.' Very often the problem is put in much more bald and extreme terms, such as 'The cost of developing the alternative site is prohibitive.' Yet many housing authorities do have the basic data from which more precise statements of cost can be obtained.

The agricultural case, too, is usually put in simple and absolute terms, such as 'Site A is first-class agricultural land' or that 'Site B is very much poorer farm land.' Very many decisions in alternative sites have been made in this country where not even basic physical agricultural data for Sites A and B have been collected.

An alternative form of comparison

Let us try to look afresh at the problem of making comparisons between two alternative sites in agricultural use, one of which is wanted for another long-term use. Immediately, we are faced with a change in the significance of the costs involved according to whether we look at it from the point of view of the individual or from the point of view of the community as a whole. To individual owners and, to a lesser extent, to local authorities when they are building their own houses, the cost of acquiring land is of some importance. Yet to the country as a whole, this cost is basically a transfer payment which has little significance in itself. The community is, or should be, much more concerned with what is known as the 'opportunity cost' of the site, which is the value of the land in the best alternative use which has to be given up if building development takes place. The ordinary individual building a house, or even a local housing authority, might well ignore this latter aspect of cost. It should not, however, be ignored, or heavily discounted by the community, as the relative value of the output of a piece of land in its present as against its possible alternative uses is fundamental to balanced land-use planning.

The significance of the costs of a direct nature may also

vary according to one's viewpoint. The cost of developing a site and building upon it are clear-cut financial costs to the housing authority. To the country as a whole, however, the true costs involved are the services which could have been rendered elsewhere by the men and materials employed by the contractor. Again, the real cost of building a housing estate is the factory, roadway or farm buildings which could have been built instead. 'Opportunity' costs of this nature are very real indeed at a time of full employment and when increased investment in capital goods is needed.

All resources used in the production of wealth, including land, are scarce in modern communities, and all resources, therefore, are subject to the concept of 'opportunity cost.' When one hears such statements as 'land in Great Britain is not fully utilised' or 'We cannot afford to have a single acre of land lying idle,' it is quite clear that the persons making such remarks do not appreciate that any use of land involves costs. It is true that if a piece of land has no alternative use it has no cost in itself, but what of the other resources which must be applied to that land before it can be brought into production? Labour and capital are scarce in all parts of the world in relation to the things that could be done with them. Indeed, in most communities labour and capital are scarcer than land itself. Those in charge of land-use planning must therefore bear in mind that society as a whole should plan for the optimum use of land combined with all other scarce resources and not merely for the best use of land taken, as it were, in isolation. Therefore, planning programmes should ideally be made in terms of resource allocation and utilisation rather than merely the utilisation of land.

It appears desirable to set up some yardsticks, embodying economic considerations, as an aid to making rational land use decisions. It is not possible, nor even desirable, to develop a single formula which could be applied to all cases of land-use competition because the nature of the problem will vary. There is, however, one method of assessing the costs and benefits involved in the problem of choosing between alternative sites of different agricultural value in relation to urban development which should be valuable in practice. It has been developed by J. T. Ward,[1] and used in evaluating a number of cases of new urban development.

A major task in such a problem is the measurement of the economic effect upon agriculture of the proposed changes in land use. Superficially, the main effect occasioned by urban development is the loss of food output, which is a loss of an annual nature, but output in this sense cannot be attributed to land alone; land, clearly, is necessary for production but then so are labour, capital and management. All these factors make their contribution to agricultural output and the employment of each of them involves costs. For example, the development of a particular 10-acre field for houses may involve the individual farmer in a loss of output of that field worth £400 gross each year. Yet it will also lead to some saving of expenditure if the farmer does not have that field. The net loss to him will, therefore, be less than the value of his annual gross output. This saving of expenditure will normally be a saving to the nation as a whole in real terms as it means that some of the resources which the farmer has formerly been using in association with the area of land to be developed will be available for use elsewhere on the 'national' farm.

The degree of loss and saving will depend upon the particular case. Where a whole farm or an area covering several farms is taken for development it is possible to use average figures for inputs, outputs and net incomes in order to make an assessment. The Annual Reports of Farm Incomes, published by the Ministry of Agriculture, Fisheries and Food, contain average figures of the kind required for many different types of farms in various parts of the country. The reports on farm incomes of particular areas and on farm efficiency standards which are made annually by the Agricultural Economics Departments of certain University centres throughout the country give both local and standard figures which can be used. It is appreciated that averages of this kind provide only an approximation to the truth and more

1 Ward, J. T., 'The Siting of Urban Development on Agricultural Land,' *Journal of Agricultural Economics*, 12, December 1957, pp. 451–66.

accurate figures are possible if access is obtained to the farm accounts of the actual land involved. Yet, even without the actual accounts of the farms concerned, very useful comparative data can be obtained by using the regional and national standard output and cost figures, providing they are allied to a systematic method of assessment and interview.

A somewhat different problem arises when, as is often the case, the site chosen forms part rather than the whole of a farm. In such circumstances average figures of a group of farms will not be pertinent, and data in the form of average returns per acre of the particular farm in question will not be sufficient because the problem involves relationships of a marginal rather than of an average nature. The loss of an individual field, or even part of a field, may have serious repercussions on the whole farm economy which are often of far greater significance than the loss of output from the individual site. This will obviously be the case where the site forms a large proportion of the total farm area and it is particularly true in the case of small farms. The effect of the loss of net output from a certain area of a farm will tend to be proportionately greater than the loss of gross output because of the high significance of fixed costs in agriculture. Buildings, machinery, and even the regular labour force tend to be fixed, particularly on the small farm, so that if acreage is curtailed, a greater incidence of the cost of these factors has to be borne by the output from the remaining acres. The only costs which may be offset are those of a variable nature, such as purchases of feeding stuffs, fertilisers, fuel and possibly farm labour which are directly related to the reduced output. In these circumstances, the measurement and the likely effect upon costs and returns is best carried out by the process of preparing a budget on each farm affected.

Though farm budgeting is a relatively skilled operation, a large amount of experience in this work has been obtained through the emphasis in recent years on farm management advisory work. The process of budgeting is used quite commonly by District Officers of the National Agricultural Advisory Service and by farmers themselves in order to assess the likely effect on their farm business of any contemplated change. The technique is simple and of particular value if budgets of only a partial nature are wanted. In these cases one only needs to know from experience the likely effect of the proposed change, and assessments can then be made of the additional costs and additional receipts which are probable. A partial budget is constructed on the assumption that the total structure of the farm business does not significantly change because of the proposed change in use of a particular piece of land. This is not always true, and in the case of land-use planning a more complete budget of the whole farm often may have to be made. If, however, only a small area of land is taken from a farm unit, a simple, partial budget is all that is necessary to assess the likely consequences.

A FARM PARTIAL BUDGET

CREDIT

The estimated new gross output from the farming change contemplated.

The costs now being incurred which will be saved by the proposed change.

DEBIT

The loss of present output likely to result from the change.

The additional costs incurred by reason of the change.

BALANCE

This will show the addition to, or reduction from, the existing level of farm profit likely to result from the proposed change.

The various steps in the analysis of competing sites can now be set out, as under:

(1) *Measure the gain to society of retaining the better quality agricultural land in an agricultural use.*

By the use of partial or complete farm budgets it is possible to assess the value of the gross agricultural output of the land in question and to deduct from it the farming expenses directly concerned with farming this particular piece of land. If the balance between the output and the variable costs is assessed for all of the sites under consideration, then the differences between these net figures reflects their value to the community in general from being in an agricultural use. Looked at in another way, an attempt is made to assess the reduction in farm profits that is likely to occur if each particular piece of land under review is taken out of farming use.

(2) *Make an assessment of the differences in the costs of building development on the sites in question.*
Some of these will arise from differences in site development, e.g. in clearing, levelling the whole or part, laying out main and service roads and excavating house foundations. Other cost differences may spring from the actual building operations involved above the foundations. Poorer agricultural land often makes poorer and more expensive building sites because of greater slope, intractable soil and subsoil, drainage problems and difficult access.

(3) *The probable additional costs of building development on the poorer site are then compared with the expected gain to the nation of leaving the better site in its agricultural use.*
The annual net benefit of retaining the best land in agricultural use can be capitalised by using a suitable rate of discount. In the case studies made at Wye College the rate used, that of 7 per cent, expressed the relationship existing at that time (1956) between net farm incomes and farm sale values. This is a market rate of discount and an argument can be advanced for a social rate of a lower level to be applied in this type of comparison.[1]

(4) *The final task of the evaluation is to review the other social costs and benefits likely to be incurred by the alternative changes of use.*
Many of these cannot be measured but some can, such as comparative transport costs between the alternative sites and places of work, shopping and entertainment. Judgment, without the help of objective measurement, has to be made on subjective matters such as loss or gain of amenity and possible change in property values in neighbouring areas. Yet it is surely important to measure what can be measured so as to reduce the field of subjective argument.

Ward has formulated this kind of cost–benefit comparison in precise terms, thus:

[1] See Chapter 10, pp. 207–11.

Let A be a site with a higher gross output in agriculture than another site B, and less expensive than B to develop for urban use.

Let C_a be the capital cost of developing Site A and C_b be the capital cost of developing Site B.

Then $C_b - C_a$ will give the additional capital cost of developing Site B. Now

Let R_a be the annual value of gross output less variable costs on Site A in agricultural use,

and R_b be the annual value of gross output less variable costs on Site B in agricultural use.

Then $R_a - R_b$ will be the benefit to the community of retaining the better site in agricultural use.

Now let V be the capitalised value of $(R_a - R_b)$

Then

if V is greater than $(C_b - C_a)$ Site A should be retained in agriculture;

if V is less than $(C_b - C_a)$ Site B should be retained in agriculture;

if V is equal to $(C_b - C_a)$ then the choice between the two sites is a matter of economic indifference.

Before we attempt to show how this method of comparison works in practice, it may be wise to query the use of money values. Though there are weaknesses in evaluating competing uses for land in money terms, it is difficult to find alternative measures which are really workable. It is not suggested that all aspects of a disputed land-use case can or should be reduced to money cost and return. To say this would be to ignore the vital though intangible factors of amenity and design; the social needs of individuals and groups and the social fabric of one area as against another. Our suggestions refer only to a quantitative method of comparing variations in the productivity of farm land with differences in the capital cost of building construction on various sites.

This is a relative comparison and not an absolute one. The market value of land should not be allowed to dominate land-use decisions. If this happens it means that certain socially desirable uses will be penalised. Thus the land uses of playing fields, other open spaces and even housing are pushed out from the centres of cities if money price alone decides. But there has been a tendency amongst some concerned with land-use planning to regard economic considerations either as matters of little significance or to feel that the economic problems have been solved overnight by the setting up of a quite complex pattern of planning authorities and planning procedures. We must remember that the planning or conscious arrangement of land uses has no justification unless it can be made abundantly clear that the end result is better than the ordinary interplay of supply and demand in the market. There is no real justification for a change in the system if the older method whereby a desired piece of land came into the hands of the highest bidder is replaced by a so-called planning mechanism in which the end result appears to be merely the replacement of the highest bidder by the man or interest who has proved the most forceful advocate.

The method suggested for comparing differences in the output of sites of different agricultural worth with the costs of using them for urban development links in closely with the idea that a balance sheet approach to land-use planning should be encouraged. Dr. Lichfield, in his recent pioneering effort in the economic aspects of land-use planning,[1] has suggested this type of approach and he gives a number of examples as to how it can be used. He also draws a useful distinction between private costs and benefits which directly impinge on, or accrue to the private developer, and social costs and benefits which have to be incurred or are enjoyed by other members of the community as a consequence of the private action of the developer.

Some cases examined

In this section the reasoning and techniques discussed in the previous paragraphs are applied to two cases where housing sites on the edge of an existing town were under

[1] Lichfield, N., *The Economics of Planned Development*, Estates Gazette Ltd., London, 1956.

dispute.[1] Both cases have been decided and development has proceeded.

Council house development on the edge of an existing settlement
Case A

In 1951 the Urban District Council of a small town in lowland Britain had a considerable waiting list for council houses and decided that there was obvious need to build new ones. The town was surrounded on all sides by agricultural land, most of which had a high natural order of fertility and was very well cultivated. The Council decided at first to build a new estate to house approximately 300 families on land that was growing arable crops, together with some top fruit, and which made up important parts of several farms. When approval of this site was asked from the County Planning Authority a nearby alternative site of low agricultural value was proposed as the result of representations from agricultural interests. This alternative site had been excavated a long time previously for brick making, and a good deal of extra cost would be involved before the land could be used for the erection of houses. The agricultural output of the land in its present use was negligible.

After objections to the use of the good farm land had been received, the local authority was persuaded to build on the alternative site and the houses had been erected by early 1954. The site used had 26 acres, and 284 houses in terraces and in semi-detached pairs were built, giving an overall density of about 11 houses to the acre. During the course of this development the many disadvantages in using the alternative site were encountered. The officers of the local authority fortunately kept careful costs of what was involved, especially of those excess costs above what they would have expected to have spent on the original site left in agricultural use (Site A), where very little site works in advance of erecting the houses would have been involved.

[1] Full details of these cases are given in J. T. Ward's 'The Siting of Urban Development on Agricultural Land,' *Journal of Agricultural Economics*, **12**, December 1957, pp. 451–66.

Some of the disadvantages of the site finally used (Site B) were:

(1) It was low-lying with a bad outfall into a nearby creek so that, although the land was not liable to flood, it tended to become water-logged. To overcome this liability, additional drainage work had to be undertaken.

(2) The poor drainage led to further trouble and expense in constructing roads which had to be sealed with a tar spray.

(3) There were a number of obstructions in the form of pits and heaps on the site which had to be cleared and levelled before building could begin. These costs of excavation and shifting were additional to what could have been expected on the other site.

(4) On parts of the site much of the top soil had been removed or rendered worthless as a result of the earlier brick working. In order to provide gardens, a considerable amount of topsoil had to be shifted from other parts of the site.

(5) Together with these additional costs over the whole site, extra expense was involved in laying the foundations to certain individual houses because of the uneven nature of the site. This was necessary in some cases because of poor drainage and in others because of large holes in the ground from which material had been previously excavated.

The broad detail of the additional costs of development involved in using Site B over the proposed agricultural Site A are shown in Table 6. It will be seen from the table that the additional capital costs involved because of the use of Site B was of the order of £6,060 or £21 for each house built.

What of the other side of the balance sheet, that is, the value of the agricultural output which would have been lost if Site A on the good land had been taken? First of all, no agricultural output on Site B would have been saved because the land was lying derelict. Site A, the original site proposed, was 25 acres in extent, and was farmed in two separate blocks by two farmers whose remaining land was some distance from the site. The loss of this site to the farming interest would have been equal to the aggregated effect of the loss of each separate block of land on the two individual farms affected.

Table 6

ADDITIONAL CAPITAL COSTS OF SITE DEVELOPMENT RESULTING FROM THE USE OF POORER AGRICULTURAL LAND

Operations	Additional capital costs		
	Total £	Per acre £	Per house £
Excavating and clearing site	1,700	64·5	6·0
Shifting and levelling top soil........	1,000	38·0	3·5
Additional drainage	650	24·7	2·3
'Sealing' roads....................	709	26·9	2·5
Total additional site costs..........	4,059	154·1	14·3
Additional cost for house foundations	2,000	75·9	7·0
Total of extra costs..............	6,059	230·0	21·3

Sixteen acres of the site belonged to a medium-sized holding growing mainly fruit, hops and potatoes. The piece of land actually concerned was used mainly for potato and corn growing. The output of the land was high and estimated to be £75 gross per acre, or £1,200 altogether. The effect of the loss of this land on the general economy of the farm was considered. Its loss would not have meant any reduction in the regular labour force involved in the whole farm, but there would have been a reduction in expenditure on casual labour and on overtime. The cost of seed and fertiliser and some machinery expenditure would also have been saved if 16 acres of land had been lost. The total estimated saving in cost was £700 per year. Taking into account the gross output and the costs saved, it was estimated that the withdrawal of the 16 acres of land from this farm for another purpose would result in a reduction in the net farm income of £500 each year.

The remaining part of Site A, i.e. 9 acres, was part of a medium-sized cash arable farm. The area concerned was in an arable rotation of three years corn interspersed with two crops of potatoes, and the gross annual output was £50 per acre, i.e. £450 in all. The farm was heavily staffed and a considerable amount of casual labour was employed during the summer time.

The effect of taking the 9-acre field away from the economy of the farm would be to make it possible to cut part of the casual labour bill of the whole farm. Again, some costs of seeds, fertiliser and machinery use would have been saved on the 9 acres if it was not cropped. It was calculated that the net effect of all these factors would have been an annual saving in costs of some £215, leaving a net loss in income of £235 per annum through the loss of the land.

The overall conclusion reached was that if Site A had been taken for urban development, the probable effect on agricultural incomes would have been a loss of about £735 a year or approximately £29 10s. 0d. per acre. It is interesting to note that the market value of Site A was assessed as lying between £100 and £120 per acre. As we are trying to make an assessment as to what is most worth while doing from the standpoint of the general community, the actual market value of a site is really of no significance in this type of calculation as, to the community, a change of use of land is only a change within, as it were, a transfer account. The market value of land is important, of course, to the private individual as it represents either a loss or a gain in potential sale income or capital.

A general comparison between the two sites and the two alternative uses can now be made. If Site A had been used for housing and Site B left as it was, the community would have saved itself a capital cost of £6,060, but it would have lost agricultural income valued at £735 per annum. By taking Site B, despite its extra capital costs on site works, the country as a whole has gained as, although through its housing accounts it has had to incur an extra charge of £6,060, the retention of the net agricultural output from Site A has added to the community's store of wealth an annual value of £735 which, capitalised at the market rate of discount of 7 per cent which was pertinent at the time of our enquiries, came to the larger total of £10,500. At a lower social rate of discount of 3½ per cent (discussed later in Chapter 10) the capitalised value would increase to £21,000. These capitalised figures are sufficiently greater than the extra development cost of £6,060 on Site B to suggest that the retention of the better land in agricultural use and the use of the more expensive site for house building were well worth while.

We have been looking only at the measurable economic costs. In practice, before any final decision is made, it is important for the community, through its local Planning Committee, to see what social costs and disadvantages are involved by both of the two alternatives. In this particular case Site B was an acknowledged 'eyesore' and therefore the local and general community gained by improving amenities. At the same time, the use of the site involved no extra distance for people to travel to and from shops, work or other centres. The social evaluation, therefore, supported the decision suggested by the comparison of real costs and returns to the community from each of the two sites.

In this particular case what the local authority decided to do has been shown to be right and proper in relation to the best use of the resources involved. Yet, looking through the history of the negotiations about this particular site, it is salutary to see that no attempt was made to measure the problem in truly comparative terms before deciding upon the course of action to take. The agricultural case was not prepared in the way we have outlined, and although a strong case was made for the worthwhileness of agricultural production on Site A, it was measured only in physical terms, that is, yields of crops, description of soil and so forth. Little of this type of description is of much value in such decisions. The local authority finally accepted Site B, because it was convinced that this was the right site to take in the national interest. But, if there had been one or more very strong-minded and influential councillors with an opposite point of view; if the town had been in a fairly well-urbanised area rather than in a strongly agricultural one; if different personalities had presented the agricultural case; one or more of these factors might well have led to a change of

Aeroplan

New urban development involves the taking of agricultural land out of food production for some time in advance of the actual construction and use of the new buildings. Housing development at Luton.

Aerofil

The British have tried to combine some new homes and jobs in carefully sited and planned 'new towns', most of which have been created since 1945. The bulk of new urban development is, however, taking place as additions to existing settlements. Harlow, Essex.

decision with Site A being developed for housing instead of Site B.

Personal experience between 1944 and 1954 in dealing with hundreds of land-use cases of such a character suggests that it is factors such as these and others, often lying outside the essentials of the case, that are responsible for the decisions made. This arises because of the impact of personalities and pressure groups on cases incorrectly presented. At the present time it is often the dialectic skill in presenting or in defending a case that is chiefly responsible for the final decision rather than the comparative strength or weakness of the different sites.

Case B

Let us look at the details of another case where again there was not much difference in the social advantage of either site. The dispute was a clear case of comparison between two sites with different agricultural outputs, but one of the sites would have required extra capital investment if it had been used for building development. Here, the local authority had been allowed to use the site which was cheapest on which to build. There was considerable agricultural objection at the time and a public local inquiry was held which confirmed the decision to use the easy site.

The site involved was a $5\frac{1}{2}$ acre field which was flat and ideal for building development. On it the local authority proposed to erect seventy houses and there was good road access to both sides of the site. The field was in pasture and formed an outlying part of a farm. The site was objected to on the grounds that it was good land and an integral part of a farm, and another alternative site was suggested with a much lower agricultural value. This alternative site had certain disadvantages for housing, thus:

(1) Drainage was a serious problem as the site was bordered by a stream and intersected by several springs and ponds.

(2) Access to it was difficult and a long sewer and long roads would be required.

D

(3) The foundations of some of the individual houses would require strengthening because the soil and sub-soil were heavy clay and on a slope.

(4) Part of the site would not be usable because of a steep slope.

The local authority, in erecting houses on the good flat agricultural land (Site A), found that the capital costs of development amounted to £5,377. This figure covered the cost of providing roads, sewers and water supply. Seventy dwellings were erected on the site comprising semi-detached, small terrace houses and a few bungalows. The overall density was at 12·2 houses per acre and the average cost of building semi-detached three-bedroomed houses on the site was approximately £1,300.

In contrast, Site B, the poor agricultural land, would have involved much heavier costs, particularly in site preparation. The extra capital cost of improving the drainage and providing a long sewer and long access road was estimated at £11,500. In addition, the site being on heavy clay, additional foundations to individual houses would have been necessary and these, at an estimate of £50 per house, involved another £3,500. Thus, there would have been a total of £15,000 of extra costs if this 6-acre site of poorer agricultural land had been used instead of the 5 acres of better land in Site A.

What of the agricultural assessment of the alternative sites? Site A, the site originally proposed and finally used for development, was a field of 5·7 acres belonging to a 62-acre holding producing mainly milk and fruit. The field was in grass and used primarily for grazing but occasionally for hay. The actual effect of the loss of this field on the general economy of the farm took the form of an increase in the purchased fodder bill. There was no reduction in the stocking of the farm. The amount of this increase in the purchase of food was estimated at £100 per year. There were, however, certain small variable costs which were saved because of its loss. These were for fertiliser, lime and tractor fuel formerly used on the site and they amounted to about £20 a year. When deducted from the additional costs involved in purchased feed, the resulting figure was £80. This represents the net return that was foregone due to the loss of Site A to the farm in question. This figure may be a little on the high side as it was thought, on examination, that the farmer's decision to replace the loss of home grown feed by purchased feed was not the most wise in the circumstances. It would well have been that an equivalent amount of feed would have been obtained at a lower cost by a slightly greater application of fertiliser and better grassland management on the remaining grassland of the farm.

The alternative site suggested, i.e. Site B, consisted of one field of $2\frac{1}{2}$ acres on a small dairy holding and three other small paddocks which belonged to various owners. The production on these three small fields was negligible. Two were only rough grazing and the third was grazed by a few geese. Thus the development of this site would reduce farming output only because of the loss of the $2\frac{1}{2}$-acre field to the small dairy farm. This field was the only one under a rotation, the rest of the holding being down to permanent grass. The rotation consisted of one year feed corn and one year fodder roots. The farm relied on purchased feed to the extent of approximately 60 per cent of all of its food requirements. Twelve Jersey cows and five 'followers' were carried on the farm so that the stocking was very intensive, although the average yield per cow was rather low. Interviews with the farmer suggested that the loss of the $2\frac{1}{2}$-acre field would not have reduced stock numbers but would have resulted in increased purchases of concentrates and hay. This increase in costs and the loss of output from the field was assessed at £45 a year. The costs saved by the loss of that actual field would have been only £6 per acre, i.e. for seeds, fertiliser and fuel. Thus, the total costs the farm would have saved was £15 in variable costs, making the net loss to the community in farm output for the loss of Site B to be £30 in all.

The two sides of the balance sheet can now be put together. If Site B had been taken, extra building costs would have involved £15,000 of capital (which would have given an annual charge on the housing authority of £800 per year).

In addition, the small farm affected by the new site would have had to bear extra costs of £30 a year. The net effect of developing the alternative site for housing would, therefore, have been to incur additional annual costs amounting to approximately £830. From this must be deducted the agricultural output which would have been left intact on Site A. This we have estimated at £80 net per annum. Thus, if the local authority had taken the poorer agricultural site because of agricultural objections to the better land, the nation would have been involved in extra annual charges of £830 minus £80, that is, £750 a year. This is a very large amount in comparison with the agricultural returns obtained or possible on either of the sites in question. On a capitalised basis, the additional £15,000 of building cost involved in using the poorer agricultural land should be compared with the capitalised differences in the net agricultural outputs of the two sites, i.e. £80 less £30 = £50, which at a market rate of discount of 7 per cent, amounts to only approximately £700. A social rate of discount[1] of $3\frac{1}{2}$ per cent would only raise the capitalised value to £1,400.

On economic grounds there can be no doubt that the local authority's decision to carry out development on the site originally chosen and to reject the alternative site of poorer agricultural value was a correct one. If the agricultural objection had been sustained, the general community would have lost quite heavily. Looking at the social costs involved, no items of importance came into the balance sheet because both sites lay roughly the same distance from the centre of the town and both fitted in fairly well with general planning considerations. Again, in this case as in the first case we have discussed, the right decision was made but the evidence presented at the local Inquiry was not in this comparative form.

The type of cost-benefit approach used in these two cases is of particular value in cases of alternatives in land-use planning where parts of farms, rather than the whole, are involved. The use of budgets to show the real effects of

1 Discussed in Chapter 10, pp. 207–11.

severance and pruning of an existing farm business is pertinent, for example, to proposals for new and improved roads.
The effect of a new motor-way on local agriculture is not
measured purely by the acreage of land taken out of cultivation. The additional effects of farm severance are important
especially when alternative routes for any road are being
considered. This severance aspect can be measured by these
farm budgeting techniques as they record the fact that on
a 'per acre' basis the loss of part of a farm can be relatively
more serious than the loss of the whole of it.

The budgeting method of measuring farm output and costs
in a changed situation certainly emphasises individual
management. As this is a personal matter concerning the
farmers now occupying the lands under discussion, it is
perhaps better to adjust the results obtained by reference to
more average yields and costs noted on other farms with
similar farming problems. In this way more allowance is
made for the land rather than for the farmers using it during
a particular period of history.

Yet, the comparisons discussed in principle and practice
in this chapter all rest on an assumption that the loss of the
agricultural output of a stretch of farming land for a long
period of time ahead is serious. This brings us to the problem
of food replacement—the need for it and possible lines of
action.

Chapter 6 Food Replacement—At Home or Abroad?

THE pressure of population on land available for food production in a country such as Great Britain depends largely upon the proportions of the total food supply to be produced by British farmers on the one hand and overseas producers on the other. The country has not been wholly dependent on its own land resources for this important use of food growing for one and a half centuries, as it has drawn heavily on the land resources of other, usually more thinly populated, countries.

Is this position likely to continue in the future? Will the nation be able to import and pay for similar quantities of its total food needs or are there circumstances in its foreign trade position which will force the British people to depend more and more on home land resources? The answers to these questions are vital in relation to the decision as to whether or not British resources of rural land are adequate and whether the release of some of that rural land to non-rural purposes is either unimportant or else a serious drain on resources.

The problem of the supply of Britain's food needs is, of course, a dynamic one that alters through time with changes in social, political and economic factors. Perhaps the most important movements have been in the size of the population, its standard of living and in the technical and economic aspects of producing and transporting foodstuffs. From early mediaeval times to the end of the eighteenth century, Great Britain was a net exporter of agricultural produce. Her main export was wool, but she also exported a certain amount of wheat and other grain. Until the end of the century, the country was self-sufficient in all of the major foodstuffs, depending on overseas supplies only for small quantities of luxury products.

By the beginning of the nineteenth century, however, the population of the country was expanding rapidly under the impetus of the Industrial Revolution, and as the pressure on the limited crop acreage intensified, the problem of feeding the new industrial workers became acute. As late as 1820 imports of wheat into this country amounted to less than 5 per cent of the home production of wheat. This was due primarily to the Corn Laws which were passed by a Parliament controlled by the wealthy landowners, and these prevented the import of grain except at high prices. The position was drastically altered by the repeal of the Corn Laws in 1846; by 1861–5 the country was importing approximately half the total wheat required in the country. At the same time imports of livestock products were becoming important.

This movement away from self-sufficiency was accentuated during the last quarter of the nineteenth century when a flood of cheap food came on to the British market from overseas. The combination of large scale and extensive agricultural systems and rapid transport by train and steamer enabled farmers in Australasia and North and South America to land food at British ports at prices below the home cost of production. The result was that by 1911–13 British agriculture provided less than one-quarter of the country's wheat requirements, two-thirds of the coarse grains, between one-half and two-thirds of the meat, less than half of the fruit and less than one-third of the national butter requirements.

This competition was encouraged by the shift of political power into the hands of the industrial leaders who accepted the creeds of 'laissez faire' and 'free trade.' Britain had become the largest industrial trading nation in the world, and cheap food pouring into the country was in part payment for the export of manufactured goods, and in part payment for invisible exports such as shipping, banking and insurance services, and interest on our extensive investments in less developed countries.

During World War I, this dependence upon imported supplies of fully one-half of Britain's food placed the country in a dangerous position. At the height of the German submarine campaign in 1917, the country's stocks of wheat fell to only six weeks' supplies. It was not until the threat reached such alarming proportions that a serious effort was made to expand agricultural production at home. The expansion, when made, was aided by a sharp rise in food prices, but the boom was short-lived and by 1921 prices had collapsed. The Corn Production Repeal Act of that year threw home agriculture back into full competition with world food supplies.

The period between the two World Wars was one of almost constant depression for British agriculture. This was reflected in the heavy fall in the arable acreages in the '20s and '30s, with a corresponding increase in the area under permanent grass and rough grazings. Yet it was during these years that there was a definite break with the free trade policy which had lasted in Britain for three-quarters of a century. A number of measures were introduced to protect the home farmer from the competition of overseas supplies. The opening move towards protection was made by the Sugar Beet Act of 1925, and then during the depths of the world economic depression between 1931 and 1933, the British Government took a number of steps to provide home agriculture with some shelter from the glut of food supplies in the world market. These measures included the Agricultural Marketing Acts of 1931 and 1933, which provided for the imposition of import duties on certain products, and the Import Duties Act and Ottawa Agreements Act of 1932, which introduced a system of protective tariffs, subject to Imperial Preference, for most goods imported into the country. In addition, subsidy schemes were introduced for wheat, and later for oats, barley, milk and fat cattle. A new type of direct grant began in 1937 with Government aid for farmers' purchases of lime and basic slag in order to encourage improvements in land fertility.

Thus, in the years immediately preceding World War II, British agriculture was already being supported by the State to some degree. Direct subsidies paid to British farmers in the three crop years immediately preceding this war varied between £11,000,000 and £16,000,000 per annum, which was between 4 per cent and 5 per cent of the gross agricultural output of the United Kingdom at that time. This apparently modest scale of relief did not represent the full support afforded to agriculture as, in addition, the prices of several major home products were maintained above free market levels by the operation of producer marketing boards and the restriction of specific imports by quotas.

Yet, even with these attempts to shelter the home farmer from the effects of world surpluses and low food prices, Britain still depended heavily upon overseas supplies for the bulk of her foodstuffs. For the three crop years 1937 to 1939 British farmers provided only 30 per cent of the total calorie requirements of the country and 45 per cent of all protein requirements. In terms of money values, the British farmer produced rather less than 40 per cent of the country's total food supplies.

The position varied greatly between individual commodities. Supplies from home acres were responsible for only 12 per cent of the total wheaten flour used, 5 per cent of all carcass meat, 29 per cent of bacon and ham, 9 per cent of butter, 24 per cent of cheese and 21 per cent of all shell eggs used. These differences in the proportion of total food supplies obtained from home sources reflected the natural protection the home farmer had for certain products because of difficulties of transport and time. For example, nearly all our liquid milk requirements and potatoes were met from home resources.

Public and political concern about British home agriculture, already quite strong in the years immediately preceding World War II, increased sharply during that war and since. The change in attitude and action from the previous century of practically unhindered 'laissez faire' in relation to home agriculture, was not dictated by the feeling of remorse for previous neglect, or in fact by a desire for self-sufficiency in food supplies on social or political grounds as had occurred in certain other countries in Western Europe. It arose mainly from the harsh realities of Britain's trading position, both physical and financial. During the 1939–45 war, all imports were severely curtailed due to scarcity of shipping, and since raw materials, weapons and certain manufactured goods had to be imported, the main cuts fell on food and, even more severely, on animal feeding stuffs. As a result it was necessary to expand food production at home, and a campaign for ploughing up permanent grassland for arable cropping, together with strong financial incentives, was initiated in the early days of the war.

Physical rather than economic criteria became all important in domestic food production. The expansion programme in home agriculture during World War II was in fact conducted with the following priorities in mind:

(1) a high output per acre of food value,
(2) a high output per man of food value,
(3) some balance between vegetable and animal products,
(4) stress on the value of protective foods,
(5) a consideration of the physical bulk of products in relation to shipping space,
(6) building up a strategic reserve of foodstuffs,
(7) considerations of good agricultural husbandry.

The priorities arranged in this list are in descending order of importance but the emphasis placed on several of them changed during the various phases of the war.

The most important physical effect of this policy was an overall increase in the acreage of arable land. This rose from the pre-war figure of nearly 13,000,000 to 19,000,000 in 1944 when the peak of war-time increased production was reached. In contrast, the acreage of permanent grass on British farms fell from roughly 19,000,000 in 1939 to 11,500,000 in 1944. At the same time there was a marked increase in crop yields, due to better husbandry techniques particularly in relation to skill in cultivations, better seed and the use of balanced fertilisers. Thus, the effect of changes both in the intensity of use to which farm land was put and in the yields obtained from crops on that land was that the gross production from British farms during the war period rose to an even greater proportion than the increase in acreage.

It was not, of course, all gain. In order to get these increased tonnages of crops, particularly of those with a high value in calories for human consumption, it was necessary to reduce other types of agricultural production in the country.

Numbers of poultry, pigs, sheep and, to a lesser extent, beef cattle were drastically cut. The numbers of milk cattle were, however, increased in support of the high priority given to milk as a protective food.

The results of these changes, in association with a reduction in average food consumption per head which, as is well known, was enforced by a stringent system of rationing, was that by 1944 Britain was producing 40 per cent of her calorie requirements compared with 30 per cent before the war, and 72 per cent of her requirements of animal protein compared with 65 per cent pre-war. For individual commodities the situation varied. The result also was to reduce the acreage of farmland required to feed any one person. This arose because of the combination of lower actual food consumption with the growing of crops of higher calorie value through the switching of emphasis from livestock to crop products, together with the improvement in yields per acre.

This overall achievement was to a large extent the result of conscious planning, and it resulted in a far greater degree of self-sufficiency in food supplies than could conceivably have come about by the operation of economic forces under free market conditions.

The post-war period

Some people may have thought that there would be a gradual return to pre-war conditions in British agriculture following the end of World War II, and there was some fear that home agriculture would once again be relegated to an inferior role. This impression seemed to result in some slackening of home agricultural production. This is especially noticeable in the sharp fall in the acreage under corn crops in 1945-6, although the requirements of sound rotational cropping were also responsible. In the year 1947, however, the country underwent the first of a series of economic crises which, unfortunately, have continued ever since. These crises have been characterised by a heavy deficit in the balance of payments account, and a consequent drain on gold and dollar reserves.

In 1947, the time of the first of these crises, the remedy

proposed was a strengthening of the export drive, coupled with an immediate cut in the level of imports. As approximately one-half of British imports were composed of food and animal feeding stuffs, while most of the remainder were raw materials which are essential for manufacturing industries and cannot be produced at home, the cut fell mainly on food and feeding stuffs, and since it was apparent that the balance of payments crisis even then was a symptom of a long-term rather than a temporary change in our trading position, a five-year expansion programme for home agriculture was introduced. This aimed at increasing once again the arable acreage so as to bring crop production, especially of corn and fodder crops, back almost to the record level home agriculture had reached in 1943–4. Combined with this was a planned increase in the output of livestock products far greater than that obtained in the war or even during pre-war years. For example, it was hoped to increase egg production to 50 per cent above pre-war level, milk output by 25 per cent, beef by 10 per cent, and to raise pig meat and mutton back to their pre-war position. The target of national agricultural net output, which had increased by 20 per cent during the war, was set at 50 per cent above the pre-war level.

The response by home farmers was most successful. By 1952 agricultural net output had risen to 52 per cent above the pre-war level, partly due to an increase in the arable acreage and partly to high yields of crop and animal production. This level of expansion was a significant achievement by British farmers for, apart from its direct contribution to the nation's food supplies which materially helped to lift food consumption from the depressed level of 1947, it indirectly resulted in the saving of foreign currency and, thereby, helped to restore the overseas balance of trade to a less critical position. It has been calculated that the marked improvement in the efficiency of our farming system over these years resulted in acting as an import-saver to the extent of £117,000,000 more of foreign exchange than at the end of the war.[1, 2]

[1] Raeburn, J. R., 'Agricultural Policy: Some Economic Results and Prospects,' *The Three Banks Review*, December 1953, pp. 3–20.

[2] Blagburn, C. H., 'Import Replacement by British Agriculture,' *The Economic Journal*, 60, March 1950, pp. 19–45.

The costs of achieving this increase in home food output and this saving in foreign exchange were considerable. The increased prices and additional subsidies offered for the capital injection in the 1947 programme were only slightly below £200,000,000, and the total direct and indirect subsidies, which had been increasing steadily since the outbreak of war in 1939, reached formidable levels of £391,000,000 in 1947–8 and £484,000,000 in the following year.

There has been considerable argument as to whether the result achieved justified the high cost involved. Some believe that it was a necessary price to pay because of the conditions ruling at that time, but others have suggested that the cost of getting this increased output and saving of dollars was excessive and has led to a high cost structure of farming in Britain which in the future will be detrimental not only to the community at large but to the industry itself. It is important to emphasise that by increasing food supplies and saving foreign currency the farm expansion programme did make a significant contribution to the recovery of the whole British economy since 1947. But it is important to note, however, that careful investigators like Raeburn and Blagburn have concluded that the process had probably gone far enough by 1952 and that any further expansion of agriculture, unless accompanied by a marked increase in efficiency and decrease in unit costs of production, would be uneconomic.

The present situation and future prospects

When the Conservative Government was elected in 1951 it was pledged to continue a policy designed to encourage a large home agriculture. Certain general lines of expansion were indicated in the following year. The level of net agricultural output was to be raised to 60 per cent above the pre-war level and this was to be achieved by 1956. This was to be done by increasing the tillage acreage by a further million acres above its total in 1952, with a substantial part of this increase being devoted to coarse grains. In addition, it was hoped to increase crop yields by a further 5 per cent and that the production and use of grass and grass products would be raised by 15 per cent. The programme involved other, more vague, targets. For example, it was intended that enough potatoes should be grown at home to satisfy consumer demand, that pig and poultry production would increase though no limit was placed on it except the limit in the increased output of coarse grains, and a general encouragement was given to further increases in beef, mutton and lamb production.

Briefly, it is fair to say that this new expansion started off in an encouraging manner but then slowed down, due to farmers' doubts as to whether the Government would repudiate the guarantees of market and price given under Part I of the 1947 Agriculture Act. This fear was intensified by the Chancellor's policy of reducing food subsidies substantially below the £400,000,000 level at which they were running in the year 1951.

In this policy the Government has been faced with the difficult problem of returning to a free market for food, with rationing and state trading abandoned, and yet at the same time maintaining the incomes of the home farmer. It has attempted to reconcile these two things by introducing a system of deficiency payments for cereals and for meat under which British farmers were to sell their main products on a free market in competition with imports but were guaranteed subsidies from the Exchequer if market prices fell below standard levels, these levels being freshly determined at the Agricultural Price Review which is held in February of each year.

This system appeared to be a fairly successful compromise in a difficult situation. Yet the amount of State help in both indirect production grants and in price guarantees during recent years has been more than £250,000,000, or about one-quarter of the total gross output of British agriculture.

In November 1956, a longer-term guarantee was given to home agriculture for those products whose prices are determined at each February Price Review. It promised not to lower the prices of any individual product by more than 4 per cent in any one year or by more than 9 per cent over three years. The total value of the prices and grants which are predetermined are guaranteed each year up to 1960 at a level that will not fall below 97½ per cent of the amount in the preceding year, after justifiable cost increases or decreases in British farming have been taken into account. In addition, a greatly increased and extended range of improvement grants have been instituted and £50,000,000 has been set aside for this type of investment in specific projects in agriculture over the next ten years. Special help is also being given to certain categories of small farmers. Thus, until 1960, the broad pattern of Government support for British home agriculture and the limits to which price changes can occur are quite definite.

The high level of State help to home agriculture, the rigid tenure system and the gap between minimum prices and the prices of competing imported foods form the crux of the present-day argument on agricultural policy. It is important to decide first on two underlying questions:

(1) What will be the relative prices of home and imported foodstuffs in the future?

(2) What are Britain's prospects of earning sufficient foreign currency to be able to purchase adequate supplies of food on the world markets?

It would be misleading to pretend to be able to forecast future price levels. All that can be done is to point out some of the main trends. Food production is increasing in all of the major exporting countries in the world and there are at the present time huge surpluses in the United States and elsewhere which have forced a reduction of cereal acreages in the United States, Canada and Australia. All the indications are that even greater supplies of cereals could be put on the world markets at current prices or with only minor increases in prices if the demand were forthcoming. The position is not so favourable with regard to livestock products, particularly beef, and it is probable that for some years ahead Britain could only import further supplies of these commodities at greatly enhanced prices.

It might be argued that this analysis takes no account of the broader issues of the problem; the fact that there is, in physical terms, a world food shortage, and that many countries which before the war were dependent upon the export of primary products are now going through a stage of industrialisation which will result in a smaller surplus of food for export. There is no doubt that the majority of the world's population have a standard of nutrition that is very low and anything that can be done to improve this standard is desirable on economic and political as well as humanitarian grounds.

Yet this should not blind us to certain realities in the situation. It is effective demand and not physical need which influences world prices of food. Those countries which are short of food are not likely to compete with us for the bulk of our foodstuffs, at least in the foreseeable future, because they do not have the purchasing power to make their demand effective. The world has also been desperately short of food in the past, even at times such as the 1930's when, though there were large quantities of cheap food, imports only flooded into the one country, Britain, which would take them and pay for them.

Though many of the so-called under-developed countries are short of food, they often have an even greater shortage of manufactured products and industrial equipment, and such countries generally prefer to spend what little foreign currency they have on imports of the latter type. In addition, there is a surplus rather than a scarcity of food in those countries best able to export supplies to the British market. In the past industrialisation has gone hand-in-hand with increased agricultural production. It is arguable that the growing industrialisation of areas such as China and India and large parts of Africa and South America will make those countries more rather than less self-sufficient in foodstuffs. Where industrialisation has been enforced, such as in some of the Eastern European countries since the last war, it usually results in some curtailment of food supplies from those particular countries. Yet on balance it does appear that the process of industrialisation will not seriously reduce the amount of food entering world trade.

The major problem, therefore, is whether we shall be able to buy the volume of foodstuffs to which we were accustomed before the war. This is the important question rather than suppositions as to whether the volume of foodstuffs would be available if we wanted to buy. The most comprehensive analysis of this problem is that made in recent years by Professor E. A. G. Robinson in his studies of the probable and desirable future level of imports.[1, 2]

Robinson's fundamental conclusion, which has received a wide measure of interest, is that if this country is to live without 'constant peril of interruption,' her economy must be adapted to manage 'on a volume of imports not much greater than four-fifths of that of 1938.' This conclusion is based on estimates of the probable volume of world trade and the share of it which this country can obtain, particularly against the growing competition of Western Germany and Japan. We should do all in our power to increase the total volume of world trade and to maintain or even improve our share of it, but Robinson is doubtful whether this approach will carry us far enough and he suggests that we should plan for long-term cuts in the volume of imported food. If agricultural output could be increased by a further 30 per cent over the next ten years—to bring net agricultural output up to double the total of pre-war food supplies—and if, in addition, imports of food were held down to 65 per cent of their 1938 level, then Robinson believes that we could feed our larger population at a rather higher standard than in pre-war days.

This argument is a powerful one though it has not met with complete agreement. Later work by Robinson[3] suggests that the saving of imports by agricultural expansion between 1938 and 1954 has been economical, particularly when judged by his estimate of the likely cost of the alternative of increased food imports paid for by increased export earnings. But what of the costs that would have to be incurred to obtain an increase in agricultural output of the

[1] Robinson, E. A. G., 'The Future of British Imports,' *The Three Banks Review*, March 1953, pp. 3–17.

[2] Robinson, E. A. G., 'The Problem of Living Within our Foreign Earnings,' *The Three Banks Review*, March 1954, pp. 3–19.

[3] Robinson, E. A. G., 'The Cost of Agricultural Import-Saving,' *The Three Banks Review*, December 1958, pp. 3–13.

magnitude that he suggests will be necessary? If this increase could be achieved wholly or even largely by improvements in the efficiency of the British farming, then we could accept the argument willingly. The evidence suggests, however, that such a further increase can in fact only be brought about at high cost which might well distort the whole economy. We might, in effect, be asked to pay too high a premium for our insurance against sudden changes in the balance of payments. There is fairly general agreement, however, that our future trading position is not going to be easy and that, as a corollary, the future prospects for British agriculture are good. Economists who have argued in detailed terms about Robinson's analysis still have to admit that they cannot foresee a situation where Britain could permanently import the relative proportion of her total food supplies which she did before the war.[1, 2, 3]

One factor which is new in the post-war situation as compared with pre-war is that all national Governments are now committed to policies of full employment. This means that their reaction to economic depression or to rising unemployment is likely to be significantly different from what it was in the 1930's. During that depression, touched off as it was by the 'crash' in the United States, Britain continued to import cheap food but prevented a heavy drain on its international account by allowing employment to fall, thereby reducing the imports of raw materials. The present full employment policy would reverse this process. In any economic recession, in order to maintain employment, we would try to maintain imports of the raw materials at a high level but to reduce those of food and feeding stuffs. With such a policy, then, home agriculture will probably attain greater rather than less security in a slump.

[1] Scott, M. FG., 'The Problem of Living Within our Foreign Earnings,' *The Three Banks Review*, June 1955, pp. 3–26.

[2] Imperial Chemical Industries Ltd., 'Agriculture in the British Economy,' Proceedings of Conference, March 1957. See especially the papers by Robinson, Tress, Nash and Raeburn.

[3] Thomas, W. J., 'Post-War Agricultural Policy in the United Kingdom,' Manchester Statistical Society, December 1958.

The position of British agriculture in relation to possible future competition from imported food can, therefore, be summed up as follows:

(1) World food surpluses, particularly of cereals products, do exist and some of these could be exported to Britain and compete directly with home-produced foods.

(2) It appears that there are many products which British farmers cannot market as competitively as can producers overseas.

(3) The profitability of British agriculture is maintained by State subsidies which make up a large proportion of the income of home farms, and a larger proportion of the incomes of arable and dairy farms than of livestock rearing farms.

(4) If British agriculture were faced with free competition from overseas without subsidies, the livestock rearing farms would not have their incomes reduced as much as the arable farms; if the farming systems remained unchanged, however, almost all types of farms in the country would become sub-marginal, at least in the short term.

(5) The nation's ability to buy cheap food from overseas is a questionable issue. The evidence suggests that Britain will not be able to increase her purchases of food from overseas much above the existing level, and even if some increase is possible, it would not be great enough to enable imported food to form the proportion of total food consumed in the country that was possible immediately preceding the last World War.

Though there is general agreement, then, that the size of home agriculture in Britain should be greater than pre-war, and that in the expansion since the war home agriculture has acted as a very valuable import saver, there is still doubt about the wisdom of further increases in home agricultural output. This doubt arises because of the fear that the increases in output will be obtained only through steep increases in the cost of production, and that the country could quickly get to the point whereby it would be using resources less economically at home by using them in agriculture as compared with using them in industry and exporting the products in order to buy food.

Coupled with this fear of excessive cost increases is the worry about the effect on overseas producers of any severe cut in imports of food arising from this policy of additional expansion in home agriculture. It could so weaken the economies of some of the more important food exporting nations that they would, not in retaliation but merely from necessity, have to cut down their imports of British industrial products. For example, a drastic cut in the United Kingdom's imports of lamb, butter and cheese would bring difficulties, even ruin, to many farmers in New Zealand. This would mean that they could not afford to buy as many British motor-cars or radio sets as before and that, by having to cut down even the purchases of goods manufactured in New Zealand, the depression could spread from New Zealand farms into their towns so that there would be a general reduction in the demand for all types of imports from Britain.

It is likely, therefore, that there will be pressure to maintain and even increase the contribution from home agriculture in Great Britain if relatively frequent crises in the balance of payments position continue. If, however, the terms of trade flow consistently in Britain's favour, criticisms of the existing level of State help to home agriculture are likely to increase.

The physical size of home agriculture

This short and incomplete appraisal of the food import situation throws some light on the need for maintenance of the existing area of agricultural land. The consensus of opinion is in favour of continuing to obtain roughly the present contribution to total food supplies from home agriculture but to press for continual increases in the efficiency of its production and the maintenance of flexibility in the emphasis on individual products.

But the maintenance of a certain level of food supplies can come from a greater, the same, or a smaller area of land under cultivation. More land will be wanted if the maintenance of food output includes within it a shift to products which have to be produced by extensive methods if this production is to become more economic. The rearing and fattening of cattle and sheep and the production of milk through the use of grass and other bulk forages, are relatively heavier users of land than the production of milk through bought-in concentrated food, the normal intensive methods of pig and poultry keeping or an emphasis on cereal and vegetable production. Less land will be needed to maintain the same level of food output in the country if the emphasis on individual products switches to the products where intensive systems of production can be economic. Less land will also suffice if there is no change in the character of production but a general rise in the output per farm and per acre through better methods of crop growing and livestock feeding. The same area of land can be adequate if more production per acre and per farm is balanced by changes in the character of production whereby products using rather larger amounts of land are grown.

We know from the discussion on future land-use changes in Chapter 4 that the agricultural area of England and Wales will lose about 600,000 acres by 1970. The production of this land, net of feeding stuffs, seeds and animals from other land, averaged £41 per acre in 1955–6. In order to replace this output the remaining land of the country will have to increase its 'net' output by about £1 per acre. The simple calculation is:

$$\frac{41 \times 600,000}{23,500,000} = \frac{246}{235} = \text{slightly more than 1}$$

Anyone who feels that this £1 an acre under-measures the size of the 1970 food replacement problem should bear in mind the contribution of the fruit and vegetables grown in the new domestic gardens of the 500,000 acres of new town growth. And though there is dispute as to the degree of emphasis to be placed on increased agricultural production from home resources, there are few who would argue for cutting it back to its pre-1939 level and few who would not be satisfied if this modest replacement of £1 per acre was obtained at a modest cost.

Chapter 7 Food Replacement—In the Domestic Garden

U P to this point in the general argument, the discussion of the effects on agriculture of an expansion of urban areas has been dealt with as if all urban uses had the same effect. But the most important use of urban land is residential—the house and, usually, its garden. Admittedly, the house may be in a number of different forms; detached, semi-detached or in short or long terraces. Yet, it is the house and its accompanying garden that is the traditional form of dwelling in Great Britain and it is certainly the form of dwelling which is predominant in new urban areas in many parts of the world. Within the centre of the larger cities, flats, either in small or large blocks, are important and are being increased, but, in relation to areas of fresh land being taken from agriculture, the individual house and its garden, is the major user.

There are in England and Wales about 13,000,000 houses and of these 2,250,000 have been built since 1945. The bulk of these new houses have been put up by public local authorities. Well under 10 per cent of the total number of dwellings erected by these local authorities have been in the form of 'flats' or apartments. The size of this recent housing drive can be appreciated if it is realised that in the period from 1931 to 1951, with only a 10 per cent increase in the population of England and Wales, there has been an increase of 32 per cent in the number of houses and flats built or made available through the adaptation of existing buildings. This increase in the number of dwellings is even larger than the increase in the number of families over that period of twenty years, the latter figure being about 28 per cent.

Thus, in Great Britain more and better homes mean primarily more houses with individual gardens (or 'yards' to use the term common in North America). This desire to live in a house surrounded by a small plot of land is often regarded as a national characteristic but it is really world wide. In a typical English suburban home the area covered by the actual house is only about one-fifth of the total area of the plot. Therefore when it is said that housing is the main user of land for non-agricultural purposes in this country, it is really the garden plot which is competing with agriculture for the use of many thousands of acres. In this competition between two forms of land use an element of food production is common to both. And to the extent that gardens are partly used for producing food crops, the loss of agricultural production from that land must be somewhat compensated for by domestic food production. But in attempting to discuss the contribution to food production made by the domestic garden in comparison with that of farm land we are entering a realm of considerable controversy.

There is little survey knowledge of how gardens were actually used or what was produced in them prior to the 1939–45 war. They were treated partly as a place of leisure and partly for the production of vegetables and fruit. With the outbreak of that war, the need for food production from domestic sources was intensified. The war-time rationing of food and its lack of variety put a premium on garden and allotment produce, and there was a great increase in domestic food production. By the year 1944 it was officially estimated that the produce from gardens, allotments and similar plots of land represented 10 per cent of all home-produced food. This gives some idea of the success of the well-known 'Dig for Victory' campaign during that war.

The scale of output of food from these domestic sources under the exigencies of war came as a surprise to many people and gave rise to the thought that even under more normal conditions the amount of food produced in gardens was probably quite considerable. Questions arose as to the amount of domestic food produced in gardens in relation to the productivity of the land in its original use as farmland. This is linked to the proportion of the area of private gardens actually cultivated for fruit and vegetables and how this changes as the size of the total house plot increases or decreases. Is there, in practice, more food grown in gardens as house plots become larger? This is an important query because one of the more obvious suggestions for conserving land in this country has been to cut down the area of land taken for housing but not to reduce the number of houses actually built.

Some of the earliest factual information on the use of gardens in this country was published in a report by the war-time Social Survey in 1942.[1] The main purpose of that survey was to discover the extent to which different kinds of vegetables were grown. A study was made of the pre-war cropping of 1,704 gardens. It was found that in the gardens of houses in towns, ten out of each one hundred grew nothing, whereas in rural housing areas only 6 per cent were uncultivated. The proportion of house gardens where flowers only were grown was, as might be expected, much larger in the towns than in the countryside, whereas those private gardens growing vegetables only were about twice as important in the countryside as in the towns. This is understandable when one thinks of the keen and competitive cultivation of vegetables by so many rural workers.

The Social Survey, at the request of the Ministry of Agriculture and Fisheries, carried out a more thorough investigation into domestic food production towards the end of the 1939–45 war. This second survey[2] provided useful information on the proportion of houses without gardens in the country as a whole and in the regional distribution of houses with cultivated gardens. The information was obtained from a random sample of households within each of forty-one towns and districts in England and Wales, the sample being stratified according to region, urban and rural district and size of town. It was found that approximately two-thirds of the houses studied possessed gardens, and that there was a much larger proportion of houses with gardens and an even greater proportion of houses growing vegetables and fruit in rural areas as compared with urban.

[1] War-time Social Survey, 'Dig for Victory,' Report No. 20, New Series, 1942.
[2] The Social Survey, 'Domestic Food Production,' Central Office of Information, 1945.

The distribution of gardens as between one part of the country and another is interesting, the relevant information for the year 1944 being given in Table 7. It will be noticed that the proportion of the houses having cultivated gardens ranged from three-quarters in the fortunate south-east of England down to roughly one in ten in the less fortunate north-west.

Table 7

THE PROPORTION OF HOUSEHOLDS WITH CULTIVATED GARDENS
ENGLAND AND WALES, BY REGION, 1944

Region	Proportion %
South-East	75
Wales	68
South	60
East	60
South-West	52
London (excluding Central London)	47
Midlands	47
North Midlands	44
North	34
North-East	25
North-West	11

The survey also showed that one in each eight houses in the towns kept small livestock (hens, rabbits and sometimes pigs) as against one in three in the countryside. Only in three gardens out of each hundred was the garden work done by a paid gardener.

The use of gardens

The first major systematic post-war investigation into the use of domestic gardens as distinct from the money value of any production involved was made by the Research Group of the Agricultural Land Service of the Ministry of Agriculture in 1951 at the time when the author was in charge of its work. Leaving aside the question of physical garden productivity, as being too difficult to measure satisfactorily, investigations were confined to the study of garden use in a stratified sample of more than 600 gardens of varying densities and types of houses in the suburban areas of London.[1] The main results of this investigation are given in Table 8 and are illustrated in Figure 3.

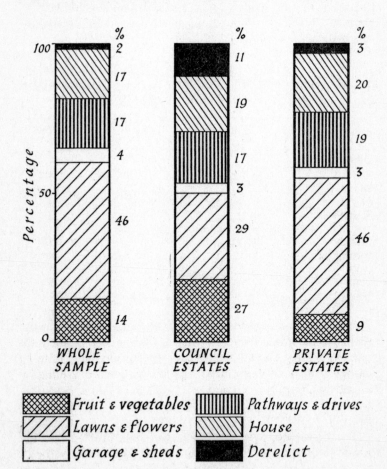

Figure 3: THE USE OF GARDENS IN SUBURBAN LONDON

[1] Mackintosh, P., and Wibberley, G. P., 'The Use of Gardens for Food Production,' *Journal of the Town Planning Institute*, **38**, January 1952, pp. 54–8.

Table 8

THE USE OF GARDENS IN SUBURBAN LONDON

Proportion of house plot* devoted to:	Whole sample† %	Council estates‡ %	Private estates‡ %
Lawns, flowers and shrubs	46	29	46
Pathways and drives...................	17	17	19
House...............................	17	19	20
Food crops (fruit and vegetables)	14	21	9
Sheds and garages....................	4	3	3
Derelict	2	11	3
Total house-plot	100	100	100

* A 'house plot' covers the area of the plot on which the house is built, together with its share of the pavement and service road.

† More than 600 houses.

‡ Samples composed of an equal number (56) of private and council houses with similar plot areas on the same type of land.

The tentative conclusions of this London study were as follows:

(1) The primary use of the gardens studied was for recreation and not for the production of food.

(2) In the special samples taken there was a marked difference in the use of gardens for food production between council and private houses. The area under food crops in council house gardens was more than double the area in private gardens.

(3) The largest areas under food crops were found in gardens on the lighter soils, irrespective of their inherent fertility.

(4) The upper limit to the area under food crops was reached surprisingly quickly as the size of house plot increased, the area cultivated tending to remain fairly constant as gardens increased in size between the net density of fourteen down to six houses to the acre. This is shown diagrammatically in Figure 4 where it can be seen that as houses with their gardens get larger, the area under the house itself, pathways, drives, garages and sheds increases

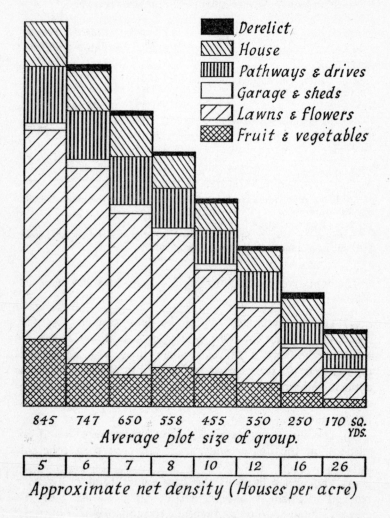

Figure 4: RELATIONSHIP BETWEEN GARDEN USE AND DENSITY OF HOUSING

relatively little. The area under fruit and vegetables is some-what greater but the bulk of the increase is taken up by lawns and flowers. Anyone who has cultivated gardens of different size in his lifetime will realise that many of these conclusions fit in with their own general garden plans and experience.

A further study made in 1953 by this research group and the research section of the Ministry of Housing and Local Government concentrated on the relationship between housing densities and domestic food production.[1] In the course of the survey, some 2,000 gardens of council houses built at various densities in the five County Boroughs of Bristol, Doncaster, Hull, Southampton and York were examined. As in the earlier survey round London, it was found that gardens and house plots varied tremendously in the use that was made of them, and that at any particular housing density there was a wide variation in the proportion of the total house plot used for growing food crops. The survey did, however, suggest that there was a statistically valid relationship between the size of a house plot and the area of it used for food production. In other words, as the size of a private garden gets smaller there is a tendency to cut down the area used for growing food crops or to cut out the growing of vegetables completely. Conversely, as house gardens get larger (within a certain size range), there was a significant increase in the area used for growing fruit and vegetables.

It is obvious from these surveys that there is tremendous variation in the use which people make of their domestic gardens. It can range from complete dereliction up to fantastically high degrees of intensive use with the garden heavily covered with glass and a large amount of double-cropping going on.

There is also a marked difference between council houses and private houses in the way in which gardens are laid out and used. In the council houses, where a large majority of

1 The *Manchester Guardian* 'Home and Gardens: Effect of House Building on Food Production,' January 13, 1955.

gardens are intensively cultivated, the garden is obviously used as an important provider of fresh vegetables. The amounts of soft fruit and top fruit are low, partly because of conditions of tenure. On the other hand, where a council house garden is neglected, the neglect tends to be complete. In private houses, however, the garden is conceived much more as an amenity feature and largely as an outside room. Where the garden is small, very often no fruit or vegetables are grown. As it gets larger the fruit and vegetables are designed to be both productive and also to look well, the vegetables being banished to the end of the garden and screened behind hedge and shrub.

The survey around London showed that, of the combination of private and council houses surveyed in that 600 odd sample, 14 per cent of the house plot area was, on average, used for food production. On a special sample of an equal number of private and council houses with similar plot areas, the proportion under fruit and vegetables was 21 per cent for the council houses and only 9 per cent for private estates. The main use of gardens of all types, whether council or private, and at all densities, is amenity and recreational, that is, for lawns, flowers and shrubs. The next heaviest use of the plot is the house itself, closely followed by the areas under pathways and drives. It is in council houses alone that the area under food crops becomes the second most important use in terms of area covered.

This difference in use in the garden of the council house tenant and the private house tenant or owner-occupier is important. If the council house tenant is a man who has received that house at a subsidised rent because of his need, it is likely that he will cultivate his garden more completely than the occupier of a private house and that he will grow not only a greater area of fruit and vegetables, but will emphasise the type of food production which produces the greatest bulk per square foot cultivated. This is particularly true in relation to the pre-war council house tenant and it must be remembered that the surveys made have dealt primarily with pre-war council houses. At the time of the London survey it was intended to look at the garden activities of the post-war council house tenant but it was found that too little time had elapsed since the building of those houses for the tenant to be fairly judged on the use he was making of his garden.

There is a basic difference between private and council houses which may influence the use made of their gardens. Very few attempts have been made to give real privacy to the gardens of council house tenants. The division between plots is usually done quite cheaply, chestnut pale or some type of wire fencing being the usual materials used. The combined use of the semi-detached house and the short and long terrace, although giving variety in the visual scene for the housing estate as a whole, usually means that the back gardens of each house abut closely on each other. When visiting a council house, one is conscious of how little real privacy there is in either the front or back garden. Little attempt has usually been made by local authorities to design or erect fencing which gives privacy. Often the planting of hedges of a shady type by tenants is not encouraged; in fact, under many local authorities, it is actively discouraged.

It is obvious, therefore, that the council house tenant is faced with a difficult personal problem. No matter what he does with his garden he will seldom be able to get privacy in his back garden. Gone, therefore, is the real incentive behind the construction of a terrace, or the laying out of a lawn. The only alternative seems to be to plan the garden in uses in which a person works rather than lazes. The main use of this type is, of course, the production of vegetables. To a council tenant, too, there is a real lack of encouragement to the planting of soft fruit bushes or top fruit trees which take a number of years to come into full bearing and which cannot be moved easily if the tenant moves on to some other district or to some other house.

This discussion about privacy in a domestic garden may seem strange and unreal to a North American reader. Houses both new and old in most parts of that continent, though often attractive in themselves and beautifully equipped inside, are yet normally set in a very open 'yard.' Both front and back gardens lie open to the service road and to the neighbours. Though this lack of privacy may seem strange to a European, it is linked with the warm neighbourliness of American people and their dislike of those who seemingly isolate themselves from other human beings by screening part or all of their garden. The seeming need of privacy in a British home is related to national characteristics which must in part spring from the problem of many people living on a crowded island. As America becomes more densely populated and more urbanised, privacy in and around the home may well become more customary and more highly prized than it is today.

There are a number of other questions about the use of private gardens which cannot be answered until more and better surveys have been made. Take, for example, the relationship between the use of a garden and the type of soil therein. One would think that gardens with light and easily drained soils would be more intensely cultivated than heavy, sticky soils. This is because most people have to garden at set times either in the evenings during the spring and summer, and/or at weekends. A soil which can be worked at any time of the day or year is obviously much better than a soil such as a clay which is temperamental and has to be cultivated only when conditions are right. Yet the evidence of the two surveys of the Research Group of the Agricultural Land Service with which the author was connected is contradictory on this point. The London survey supported the idea that gardens with light soil were handled better than those with heavy soil. The surveys of council house gardens in the five County Boroughs, however, suggested that the reverse was true. There were differences between these two surveys in the type of houses and tenants studied and in the parts of Great Britain visited. When two surveys give different and contradictory results the thing that is quite certain is that there is a good case for further investigation. It is a great pity that no further investigations on this or any other major aspects of garden use have been made in this country in the years since 1956.

In addition to this lack of real knowledge as to how the

Though the fronts of many new housing estates have a pleasant appearance, the use of terrace houses, the open type boundary fences and the absence of trees gives a sad lack of privacy and space in the back gardens.

Private gardens are used in a variety of ways. Here are two long gardens side by side. The one on the left is used heavily for the growing of fruit and vegetables. The one on the right is designed more for amenity purposes—the relatively few vegetables being banished to the end of the garden and hidden from view by screening hedge and scrub.

use of gardens changes with different types of soil, there is probably a relationship between the income group of an occupier and the use he makes of his garden. One would expect that people with lower incomes would grow a higher proportion of vegetables and that as incomes rise the vegetable portion would decline in relative importance, though possibly remaining the same size in area as the total garden plot increases. It might also be expected that soft fruit and top fruit would begin to come into gardens as they get larger and as they are occupied by people with higher incomes who enjoy a more selective diet. Again, it may well be that there is a close relationship between the use of a garden and whether or not it can be easily overlooked by its neighbours. All of these are relationships about which we can surmise but on which there is no good evidence.

Take, again, the great variation in the number and use of gardens in different parts of this country. Surely there will be differences in use between the north of England where gardens are not customary as compared with the south where gardens have been available to three-quarters of all family households. The use of a garden, and becoming a good gardener, particularly in relation to an attractive layout, is not something that is innate or born to a Briton, although to hear some Britons talk one would think this to be true. No, like so many other things, skill in gardening and sensitivity and competence in garden design come from considerable experience, practice and background. Is it so surprising that, in north-west England, with only one house out of ten previously having had a garden, local authorities are having trouble with a large number of derelict gardens on the new council housing estates? How many generations will be necessary to make people and families with no tradition of a private garden responsive to one and careful and thorough in its use?

The productivity of gardens

Productivity is very different from use. The two are very different in farming and they are also very different in gardening. As far as can be seen from the various surveys

E

made of garden use, a cross-section of council and private houses in certain towns, and in the year 1951, showed a conservative average of about 14 per cent of each house plot used for the production of vegetables and soft fruit. There is sometimes an additional production of food resulting from the keeping of small livestock in many gardens, such as the hen and the rabbit. The first step in measuring garden productivity is to relate the area of land used for growing food in gardens with the area of land which is taken out of farming use when a housing estate is built and laid out. When urban development encroaches on to agricultural land, the extent of the area still used for growing food is considerably reduced, although it is far from being extinguished. Although gardens and allotments are almost wholly limited to the production of vegetables and fruit (mainly soft) and flowers with occasionally some small livestock, it would be wrong to compare their production with that of market gardening on the grounds that general farms produce different commodities, such as cereals, milk, meat and other livestock products. As seen in Chapter 4 it is only in a small number of cases that new urban development takes place on land devoted to market gardening. Most of it, in fact about 90 per cent, occurs, and is likely to occur on better than average farm land which is mostly used for dairy and arable farming. For this reason an estimate of the output from general purpose farm land of better than average quality should be used for purposes of this particular comparison.

But is it correct to compare the output from an acre of better than average quality farm land with 14/100ths of that acre devoted to the growing of vegetables and soft fruit? This would be a fair comparison only in relation to the building of an estate entirely made up of houses with their service roads on a fresh piece of agricultural land. In the discussion of the types of new urban development, however, it has been shown that housing, although the major use, is only one of such uses. There are the other urban uses, such as industry, schools, shops, major roads, parks and playing fields. Although the land under these uses will, in some cases, still be of potential food production value, in normal circumstances, and with the exception of allotments, there is no food produced on them.

Although the proportion of these other urban uses varies tremendously from one town to another, the analysis made of future Development Plans in the cities and larger towns of England and Wales suggests that about half of the land taken for major urban uses in the next twenty years or so will go to housing development. Broadly then, for every acre taken for housing another acre will be taken for other major urban uses. This means that when farm land is taken for urban development only about some 7 per cent of the land is likely to remain in cultivation for food.

There is, unfortunately, no exact information on the productivity of gardens as distinct from their use. The only estimate available is one derived from National Food Survey data. For each year during and since the 1939–45 war the Ministry of Food (now the Ministry of Agriculture, Fisheries and Food) has made reports on domestic food consumption and expenditure. These reports have been compiled from information obtained from a random sample of several thousand households in representative urban and rural areas in different parts of the country. Those participating in the scheme are asked to record the weight and money value of every item of food consumed each week, including vegetables, fruit and other produce 'obtained from gardens and allotments, and as gifts or purchases.' The proportion of such 'free' food which is obtained from other than domestic sources is very small. This free food is valued at the average price which is paid by housewives for similar purchases at the time of survey.[1]

Upon the basis of this information, the Research Division of the Ministry of Housing and Local Government attempted to calculate the domestic output of food for each acre under ordinary houses with their gardens. At a density of twelve houses to the acre, the figure came out at just under £6 a plot or a gross total of £67 10s. 0d. in the year 1951–2. This represents £480 on a cultivated acre basis, excluding the

[1] Ministry of Agriculture, Fisheries and Food, 'Domestic Food Consumption and Expenditure,' Annual Reports of the National Food Survey Committee, H.M.S.O.

value of flowers and livestock products. In the bulletin 'The Garden Controversy,'[1] it is pointed out that this basis of estimation has many weaknesses in it and it has been found more satisfactory to look at the estimates made of the value of food produced on allotments. Estimates of money values have had to be used because of scanty information on physical yields and the difficulty of making satisfactory calculations on a calorie basis. The mere calculation of the weight of produce grown per acre takes no account of the actual food value of different products so that differences in carbohydrate, protein, fat and vitamin content of different foods are not fairly evaluated by these means.

Estimates on the basis of a cultivated acre of the value of food produced by allotments vary from a high figure of about £560 down to £300 per acre. If the lower figure is taken as the output of reasonably tended allotments, this value can then be assigned to the parts of the domestic garden which are used to produce vegetables and fruit. This estimate errs on the cautious side. This is important because of the great variation from the average which occurs in garden use and the difficulty of allowing for wastage and other aspects. This figure of £300 per cultivated acre is, it must be remembered, a valuation of the produce grown and used at its cost to the housewife of getting alternative supplies, or in other words, at retail prices.

Is it correct to use retail prices for food in calculations of the monetary output of gardens as against better than average quality farm land? The category of prices used should depend upon the sort of comparison made. If we were solely concerned with a direct comparison of the physical productivity of gardens and farm land, then the same category of prices should be used throughout, i.e. both at retail or both at wholesale. But this is too limited a comparison because the problem involves the worth of produce to the actual consumer. There are a number of steps in the marketing chain between production on the farm and the consumer. There are very many fewer steps

[1] Best, R. H., and Ward, J. T., 'The Garden Controversy,' Department of Agricultural Economics, Wye College (University of London), August 1956.

between what is grown in the domestic garden and the use of it on the domestic table.

Vegetables produced in the garden are available for immediate consumption, and, incidentally, have the great advantage of being completely fresh. The housewife growing her own vegetables is clearly saving the retail price of food she would otherwise have to buy at the local shop. It is, therefore, logical to value garden output at retail prices. Some people might suggest that if the housewife did not have these vegetables in her own garden she would not buy them at the shop. This is debatable. It is true that for the luxury and less habitual type of vegetable, like salads, many people will do without when they are not available in their own garden. In relation to the bulk of common vegetables, however (things like peas, carrots, beans, cabbage and potatoes), if they are not available in the garden, then housewives will usually buy from the greengrocer.

The position is different in the case of food produced on the farm which has to be marketed before it is available for consumption. Marketing is much more complex than is generally realised. It is a highly organised and costly process which may well involve a sum equal to the cost of producing that food on the farm. This is reflected in the fact that farm gate prices for food products are, on average, only 40 to 50 per cent of the retail prices of such products.

To be strictly accurate, we should consider not only the costs of marketing and differences therein between garden and farm produce, but also the costs of producing food in gardens as against those on farms. This is a complex problem which cannot be dealt with adequately here.

The information is, also, so meagre that it is better to leave costs of production out of the argument but to include as an addition to the farm gate price the marketing costs which have to be incurred by farm produce before it is available for consumption.

The gross output of better than average farm land, the type used for urban growth, at 1953–4 prices was about £45 per cultivated acre, at farm gate prices. The value of the production of the land used for vegetables and fruit in gardens was £300 per cultivated acre, using the same year but retail price levels. At wholesale prices, the garden production would amount approximately to £150 to £180 per cultivated acre. But as emphasised earlier, on average, only 14 per cent of each house plot is used for vegetables and fruit production. Therefore, in an area covered with houses at about twelve to the acre, the value of production per acre at retail prices is about £42 and at wholesale prices about £21 to £25. This can be contrasted with the figure of £45 for better than average farm land at farm gate prices. Though this comparison is valid in looking at small scale residential development only, it has been pointed out in Chapter 3 that on balance, housing comprises about one-half of all new major urban uses. On this basis the relevant value is the production of 7 per cent of the total area of farm land taken for development. The output of food from urban acres is thereby reduced to some £21 at retail prices or about £12 at wholesale prices as against the value from better than average farm land at £45 per acre.

Garden food production and the density of new housing

We must be careful not to construe this garden argument so as to suggest that gardens are a good use of land no matter how large they may become. General observations suggest that there is considerable wastage of land in gardens when they are one-fifth of an acre and above in size. But special surveys would have to be made to see how much waste there is and what is the crucial point at which the value of the fruit and vegetables grown ceases to outweigh the physical waste of land area which has been taken from farming use.

If we look at the garden-farm land argument in relation to the more customary range of housing densities, that is, between fifteen and five houses to the acre, it seems that the best compromise between the amount of farm land being used and the return in food production from the house gardens is secured at somewhere near a mid-point, that is, at around ten to twelve houses to the acre.

Suggested decreases in the amount of land needed for new

housing can only be obtained if there is a sharp decrease in the area of land allowed in each plot. This involves a change-over from semi-detached houses to a combination of flat development with some terrace houses. Table 9 which has been adapted from data given in a well-known official planning manual,[1] shows that a limit is quickly reached in increased housing density if garden plots of any size are to be retained. The table shows that, as compared with houses at ten to the acre, any rearrangement of density to bring the number up to thirteen to the acre in order to save a quarter of the previous area used will involve an arrangement of terrace houses and flats in a proportion of four to one. In order to save one-half of the land required for housing a certain number of people, it is necessary to abandon the detached and semi-detached house altogether and fill up the site with 20 per cent of terrace houses and the remaining 80 per cent in high flats. This means the practical abandonment of the domestic vegetable plot if housing densities are to be tight enough to lead to major savings of open agricultural land.

Food production and urban uses other than housing

Reasons for the relatively small proportion of land that is saved by increases in housing density are to be found in the urban uses which lie outside of housing. Of the urban expansion foreseen in the near future, half will be accounted for by new and rearranged housing and the remainder will be in 'other' urban uses.

These other uses are expanding in their own right. Changes in them also tend to be different from variations in housing. In new town Development Plans, public and private open spaces of one sort and another, outside the domestic garden, will be taking up one acre in each five of the new land proposed. If housing areas were further constricted it would be reasonable to expect, on the basis of what has happened in densely built-up areas in various parts of this country, that the reduction of house size and of garden plot would

[1] Ministry of Housing and Local Government, 'The Density of Residential Areas,' H.M.S.O., 1952.

Table 9

SAVINGS OF LAND UNDER VARIOUS FORMS OF HOUSING IN A
TOWN OF 25,000 POPULATION

Type of development	Population	Gross residential density (persons per acre)	Gross residential area (acres)	Saving of land	
				Acres	% of gross residential area
1. Inter-war standard of about 10 houses per acre (datum)	25,000	26·6	940	0	0·0
2. Free use of terrace houses	25,000	32·3	774	166	17·7
3. 20 per cent medium flats, 80 per cent terrace houses	25,000	34·7	720	220	23·4
4. 40 per cent medium flats, 60 per cent terrace houses	25,000	38·4	651	289	30·7
5. 60 per cent medium flats, 40 per cent terrace houses	25,000	44·4	563	377	40·1
6. 80 per cent high flats, 20 per cent terrace houses	25,000	56·9	439	501	53·3

mean a stronger demand for more small open spaces within the residential area as children's playgrounds. Again, the side roads to the houses would be used much more heavily for children's play, and one-way and 'no traffic' streets will be more necessary and more common. The demand for allotments will be stronger because of the lack of large back gardens. School and public playing fields will be greater necessities. With more people living in a particular area of land who will want to get in and out of it for work and shopping, more space will have to be allowed for transport and communications. The usual trend is, therefore, for the

non-housing urban uses to stay the same or increase in area
as house-building densities increase.

The strong pressure for more open space for people to
enjoy in towns arose from the protests of individuals with
a social conscience and the more radical political parties
against the legacy bequeathed to us by the early years of the
Industrial Revolution. The tightly packed areas of housing
with little room for the activities of either children or adults
can be seen in industrial towns through the length and breadth
of the country, and particularly in the northern cities.
People are crowded into long rows of terrace houses, with
small paved yards and alley ways. Little green is to be
seen except for the ubiquitous laurel and a few window
boxes, and children play in the dirt of the alley and the risk
of the main street.

The more liberal allocation of open space for public
needs in the town plans of the future is obviously desirable.
But the existing provision of open space, and the needs for
more of it, vary tremendously from one locality to another,
and to a greater degree than do the provision or needs of
housing. The public open space available in a town depends
so much on historical accident and on historical farsighted-
ness. Private benefaction of large open spaces; long-sighted
planning many years ago as, for example, in the provision
of the large London parks; the degree of access to open
space of a private character which also satisfies public
demand; all such factors are of varying significance in local
situations and produce contrasting problems between towns.
Consider, for example, the basic difference between the open
space needs of crowded communities in the East End of
London and those in the narrow mining valleys of South
Wales. In the first case there is no rural lung, no stretch
of land to which a person can escape from the crowded
housing and industrial areas of that part of London. In the
other, the equally crowded but strip settlement of a valley
such as the Rhondda is mitigated by the large areas of open
and wild mountain-side and moorland which are a stone's
throw from the busy, crowded streets of the mining towns.
This incongruity between dense habitation and extensive land

use is typified by the mountain sheep which spend much of their time wandering along the backs of houses searching the dustbins for delectable morsels.

Normally, public open spaces make no refund to the community in terms of food production when they are taken out of agricultural use. This means that open spaces cannot be regarded in the same way as the private garden. There is the one important exception. In times of national emergency such as a war and a real physical threat to the food supplies of a community, these public open spaces can be turned, in part or whole, to the growing of food crops. This happened to a considerable degree during the World War of 1939–45 when a large number of war-time allotments were carved out of parks in cities and made available at very low rents to ordinary citizens who wanted to augment their private food supply. The type of food that can be grown is, however, very limited in relation to the range of agricultural and horticultural products which are obtained from commercial farms and commercial market gardens. This is also true of the range of food products grown in the domestic garden. Bulk vegetables and greens are the main contribution, though cereals can be and were grown in some of the larger areas such as parts of the big parks. Public open spaces are obviously difficult to use for types of food production where trespass is a serious limiting factor. The keeping of sheep and dairy cows and other cattle, the growing of soft and hard fruit and crops making heavy use of glass are seldom practicable in such areas.

The future holds so many possible changes in personal habits. Who can foretell the importance placed on the private garden by future generations? If standards of living rise will the home growing of vegetables and fruit lose out in competition with frozen and pre-packed supplies from commercial sources so that the English garden becomes an outside room designed to give only intangible satisfaction?

It does seem likely that the non-housing uses of land by townspeople will continue to grow in importance and that large areas of town and countryside will become private and public open space. Here is a demand for land which, though it can give happiness to many, means in practice a complete switch to a non-food use except in times of national emergency.

The next stage in this discussion of the impact of urban growth on agriculture and food production is to look at the practical possibilities of bringing in new land into agricultural use in order to replace the erosion by urban demands of the existing stock of farm land. The largest potential area lies beyond the present margin of cultivation in the hills and uplands of the west and north of Great Britain. Is it here that we should look for land and food replacement?

Chapter 8 New Land—From the Hills?

ALL countries, no matter how intensively exploited, have areas of land which are on the margin of cultivation. These frontier areas are broadly of two types. There are first, the small pieces of land which have proved difficult to exploit in the past and which have been left behind in an extensive use as man has settled and cleared the lowlands. There are many such areas of coppice, shaw, odd parcels of land, wet bog, tidal flat, which must mount up in total area to millions of acres even in a country as small as Great Britain. We shall examine these more critically in Chapter 9. The second and larger area is the land, primarily in the hills and uplands, which is on or beyond the margin of existing cultivation.

There is an important distinction to be made here between the margin of cultivation and the margin of profitability. The former is always with us even in the most intensively cultivated areas although it varies greatly through time. All cultivated land touches or is surrounded by uncultivated land of one form or another—the rough grazings on the hills, odd uncultivated plots on lowland farms, tidal areas along the coast and the outer suburbs of towns and cities. At any particular time the cultivated land adjoining that which is uncultivated could be said to be at the margin of cultivation. It is a fluid line through time because of the pressure of social, economic and physical forces.

One of these changing forces is the development of new techniques and systems of husbandry which enable land previously beyond the margin of cultivation to be successfully cultivated. Examples which have been important in land reclamation are the invention of the tile drain, the stump jump plough, the discovery of important trace elements, aerial top dressing with fertiliser, new strains of grasses and clover, and new methods of grassland sward establishment.

Yet any person owning or using rural land is more vitally concerned with the margin of profitability than the physical margin between different levels or types of cultivation. A profitable farm or estate may well have large areas of uncultivated land on it. The margin of profitability depends on the efficiency with which resources are used in farming, and land is only one of these resources. This is why some farms are well above the margin of profitability even though they are close to the margin of cultivation. For example, the larger hill farms in Wales in the early 1950's were earning higher profits than the smaller and lower lying farms on inherently more fertile land of the Welsh uplands and borders.

It is important to remember that both the margins of cultivation and of profitability are flexible. Even so, the margin of profitability is essentially a short-term concept in comparison with cultivation and, in particular, with potential cultivation. The level of profitability is related to many factors which can change in a relatively short time—relative price levels for agricultural products, size of farm unit, personal efficiencies and personal standards of values. There are also many difficulties of a social nature which are involved in the improvement of agricultural areas which are close both to the margin of cultivation and to the margin of profitability. Such a description has been broadly true for the hills and uplands of Great Britain for many years.

Land reclamation and improvement in the hills and uplands

An appraisal of large parts of the highlands of Wales, Scotland, the Border country and the Pennines will show a combination of high altitudes, rigorous climate, poor drainage and thin soils giving rise to poor land. These physical limitations affect the choice of farming systems by restricting it to types like sheep and cattle rearing which employ relatively few people. The land has been settled in the form of isolated farms and hamlets with rather few villages or towns. Accessibility is poor, and social and physical isolation, coupled with a history of low levels of agricultural and personal incomes and in living facilities for most of the rural population, has led in the past to a gradual loss of people, especially in the younger age groups. Many of the hard core areas of chronic rural depopulation are found in these hills and uplands. The general result is that not only do fewer and fewer people live in these areas but an increasing proportion of those who remain are old people, who are disinclined to change. This ageing of the population has, of course, been common all over Britain of late years, but its effect has been more marked in isolated country districts of this type.

It is clear, therefore, that many of the upland areas suffer from a variety of drawbacks which are so closely interrelated that they constitute both cause and effect at one and the same time. There are two vicious circles present, one of which results from the husbandry and economic difficulties of farming in such areas, and the other through weaknesses in the population and social structure. These are shown, in a simple diagrammatic way, in Figure 5[1] and they represent the interrelated problems that occur in areas such as central Wales and the Scottish Border.

We are dealing here with parts of Great Britain which are large in extent but small both in their agricultural output and in their local populations. A recent study made at Wye College attempted to measure the agricultural contribution of these areas.[2] The hills and uplands cover roughly 14,000,000 acres which is one-quarter of Britain's land surface. It is a rather higher proportion (31 per cent) of all the land in agricultural use in the country. This huge area of land is farmed in roughly 40,000 holdings and these represent more than one in ten of all farms above one acre in size in the country.

The overall agricultural output of the hill country is relatively low. Though it is one-quarter of the total land surface, the land provides only 4 per cent of the total agricultural output of the nation. Even its contribution of livestock, measured as a proportion of all fatstock slaughtered in this country, is only between 5 per cent and 7 per cent of the total because its large contribution to sheep slaughterings

[1] O'Connor, B. A., and Wibberley, G. P., 'Social Problems in the Development of Livestock Rearing Areas,' *Journal of the Ministry of Agriculture*, **59**, 1953, pp. 564–70.

[2] Davidson, B. R., and Wibberley, G. P., 'The Agricultural Significance of the Hills,' *Studies in Rural Land Use*, Report No. 3, Wye College, 1956.

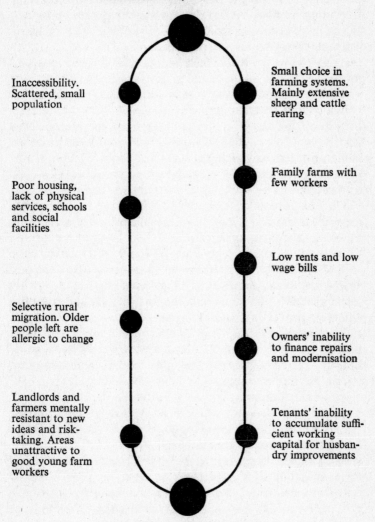

Basic physical limitations (high altitude, steep slopes, poor aspect, excessive rainfall, poor drainage, thin leached soils)

Small choice in farming systems. Mainly extensive sheep and cattle rearing

Inaccessibility. Scattered, small population

Family farms with few workers

Poor housing, lack of physical services, schools and social facilities

Low rents and low wage bills

Selective rural migration. Older people left are allergic to change

Owners' inability to finance repairs and modernisation

Landlords and farmers mentally resistant to new ideas and risk-taking. Areas unattractive to good young farm workers

Tenants' inability to accumulate sufficient working capital for husbandry improvements

Low output per acre and per farm. Small population with low standards of living

Figure 5: THE CYCLE OF EVENTS IN MARGINAL FARMING AREAS

is heavily overweighted by its low contribution to the total home supplies of cattle, calves and pigs.

The study did show the major contribution made by hill sheep and wool to national home supplies of these products. In the hills and uplands there is a breeding flock of about 4,500,000 head which provides each year, in addition to its own replacements, some 2,500,000 to 3,000,000 sheep to the lowlands. In total, these make up between one-third and one-half of the total sheep slaughtered in one year in the country, though their monetary value is only about one-quarter of the total because of the small size of hill sheep and the large proportion of store animals in the contribution. Again, the hills and uplands are responsible for about one-third of the annual value of the whole produced wool clip of this country.

The magnitude of this contribution comes clearly into focus if an attempt is made to assess the effects of a cessation of hill and upland sheep farming. Such a cessation would force the total sheep population of the country down from its present level of 20,000,000 to between 10,000,000 and 11,000,000 head. Even with rearrangements of land uses on lowland farms, the lowland sheep industry would in such a situation probably settle down at below two-thirds of the size of the present national sheep flock. It might, however, be able to get to above two-thirds of the size of the existing industry in terms of weight of mutton and lamb produced and in the money value of its sheep and lamb sales.

The contribution of the high grounds of Great Britain in relation to cattle and beef is very different to that in sheep. About 100,000 beasts leave the high country each year from truly beef breeding herds. They are joined by another 150,000 which come from the dairy herds now scattered through the hills and uplands. Yet these in total make up only between 5 and 7 per cent of the United Kingdom's production of cattle for slaughter, and because so many of the animals are calves or stores, the money value of the contribution is below 4 per cent of the national figure. This output is low enough to suggest that Britain would not have insuperable difficulties in maintaining her cattle supplies if the present contribution from the high ground was lost, unless severe difficulties arose in the extensive trade in cattle from Ireland.

It is well known that milk production has become important in farming systems through much of the hills and uplands of this country. From this one-quarter of our land surface flows about 40,000,000 to 50,000,000 gallons of milk each year. Although this is only 3 per cent of the national annual milk sales, its money value to the particular farms concerned is close to the value of their sheep sales and greater than the value of the cattle sold from Britain's high land. Though this quantity of milk could probably be replaced in the lowlands without causing severe difficulties if milk production stopped on the high land, the loss of the regular milk cheque would be severe on many small upland farms. It would take away nearly one-fifth of the total agricultural income of the farms concerned—and this the most dependable part.

What is the cost to the country of obtaining this agricultural output? The estimates made in this study suggested that the value of the resources used in hill and upland agriculture is greater than the value of the gross output obtained and that such an unsatisfactory position is maintained by a group of farmers accepting a standard of living lower than that of the rest of the community. Another interesting conclusion was that, apart from the sacrifice made by the upland farmer in accepting a lower standard of living, there was no evidence to suggest that the rest of the nation was paying more in the way of subsidies to support agriculture in the hills and uplands than was being paid to support lowland agriculture. The proportion of the national agricultural subsidy bill paid to farms on the hills and uplands is in fact slightly lower than their proportionate contribution to the national agricultural output in money terms. In addition, each of the farmers in these areas receives, on average, a much lower sum of Government assistance than does his counterpart in the lowlands. This means that instead of the subsidy policy of the State tending to equalise net farm incomes between farmers on the low ground and those in the hills, the actual effect is to widen the gap between them, as the lowland farmers, who are more efficient in using their resources in farming, also receive a proportion of total subsidies rather greater than their production would appear to warrant.[1]

It is clear that this large part of our countryside is producing relatively little food for us. Yet it is obviously playing a key part in the sheep economy of the whole countryside. Its production is concentrated on livestock products, and meat is something of which we are still relatively short in terms of home production. Therefore, there would seem to be scope for improving the use of farm land in the hills and uplands and bringing in some of the land now in rough grazing into the cultivated area of the farms. Certainly, the opportunities for land reclamation are superficially great because, of the 14,000,000 acres of hills and uplands in agricultural use, only 2,250,000 are in crops and grass, leaving 11,500,000 acres in rough grazings, much of this being unenclosed.

These opportunities for 'new' land in the hills must appear large and even favourable to those visitors from the towns who, when they visit the hill country, usually travel through it on a summer day when the sun has burst through the clouds and the landscape is full of colour, space and seeming promise. These are the people who do not know or else forget the vicious and interrelated cycles of physical, economic and social problems with which these areas constantly have to contend. As people in all communities measure what is worth doing and where it is worth living by relative standards, the hill country loses out constantly to the more favoured areas of the lowlands where life in terms of farming possibilities and human settlement is kinder and easier and where there is a larger margin for success.

The bulk of the high country is in natural and semi-natural grassland. It is obvious that a careful examination by persons skilled in grassland research and grass management is

[1] These suggestions as to the incidence of subsidies are still under discussion by research workers. See, for example, Attwood, E. A., 'Agricultural Subsidies and the Hill Farmer,' *Journal of Agricultural Economics, Great Britain*, **13**, June 1959, pp. 329–33, and subsequent replies.

needed to assess the practical possibilities of improvement. A considerable amount of attention was paid to the ecology of grass by Sir George Stapledon and his colleagues at the Welsh Plant Breeding Station at Aberystwyth in the 1920's and 1930's. Here, there developed a unique combination of careful and long-term research together with a missionary zeal towards the possibilities of the better use of Britain's hill country. It is salutary to realise that Sir George Stapledon advocated a greatly improved use of Britain's hill country at a time when the economic winds blowing across Britain's agriculture were very cold, and food surpluses and low prices were making most farmers concentrate on the use of their best pieces of land only or on attempts to run their farms on extensive systems with costs kept to a very minimum. It is interesting to ponder on the effect this great agricultural missionary would have had if he had been producing his evidence and exercising the force of his persuasive personality at a time and in an economic climate more conducive to a substantial increase in the area of cultivated land in this country.

Suggestions as to the physical possibilities of improvement on this poor, high land must be considered against its background of social difficulties and economic marginality. The important question for the individual farmer and for the nation is the net income left on hill and livestock rearing farms when costs have been met. This is, in effect the amount available to the farmer as wages for his own work on the farm, as interest on the capital he has invested and as a reward for running the business. It is a residual amount, the difference between the gross output of the farm and the farmer's total expenses. If we exclude the Scottish crofts, which are rather unusual both in their farm production and their costs, Table 10 shows the position on more orthodox farms on high ground in this country during three consecutive years.

It will be seen that this net income was a minus quantity in one of these years and in the two years when it was positive it was at a low level. In no year did it exceed the minimum wage rate of an agricultural worker in this country. In actual fact, the amount of cash available in the farm-house has been

Table 10

THE INCOMES OF HILL AND UPLAND FARMS*

	1950–1 £'000	1951–2 £'000	1952–3 £'000
Gross Farm Output	34,108	39,677	43,252
Farm Costs....................	35,281	37,475	35,505
Net Farm Income..............	−1,173	2,202	7,747
Net Income per Farm	−£37	+£69	+£245

* 31,683 farms, excluding crofts.

larger than the totals shown, as family labour has been charged as an expense in the calculations whereas in practice it is often not paid. Again, many farmers in the hills and uplands are owner-occupiers and therefore do not pay rent, though this is included in all calculations of farm incomes. Yet rents, in practice, are so low that even when they are not paid they leave little extra income after necessary repairs to equipment and farm buildings have been made.

During these same three years the net incomes of farms on the lower and better lands of England, Wales and Scotland were around the £600 level. This means that even in the best of the three years 1951, 1952 and 1953 the average net income of farms on the high ground was only one-third that of the more fortunate farmers on the lower land. If an allowance is made for the manual work done by farmers and wives on both lowland and highland farms, it is possible to make a reasonably close estimate of the efficiency with which all farm resources are used, that is, the efficiency of the use of the land, capital and the people who are working on them. The relevant information is given in Table 11.

Broad calculations of this sort always involve a degree of hidden error but as far as possible the assumptions made in the compilation of this table have been consistent with both hill and lowland groups of farms so as to isolate the relevant differences. In not one of the three years studied did the value of the farm output in the hills and uplands exceed the value of all resources, human and material, which were used. On lowland farms, however, the resources used have been rewarded by an output greater than real cost.

Table 11

THE RELATIVE EFFICIENCY OF FARMING ON UPLAND AND
LOWLAND FARMS (INCLUDING CROFTS)

	1950–1 £ million	1951–2 £ million	1952–3 £ million
Hills and uplands:			
Gross output	37	43	47
Total costs	37	40	37
Value of work done by farmer and wife	11	12	13
Value of total resources used ..	48	52	50
Gross output per unit of re- sources used (X)............	0·77	0·83	0·94
Lowlands:			
Gross output	993	1,078	1,155
Total costs	699	787	846
Value of work done by farmer and wife	139	150	156
Value of total resources used ..	838	937	1,002
Gross output per unit of re- sources used (Y)............	1·18	1·15	1·15
Efficiency on hill and upland farms in comparison with those of the lowlands $\frac{(100) \times X}{Y}$	65	72	82

The trend is, however, somewhat different from that of
any one year. Whilst the efficiency of farm production
remained relatively constant in the lowlands during the three
years studied, it improved quite rapidly in the hills and
uplands. Thus the ratio between the efficiency of the two
areas of farming moved in favour of high-land farms. This
improvement must, however, be treated with caution as
variations in farm output and in the resources used are
normally much greater in areas with difficult physical conditions than in others. Actually, during these three years, the
structure of farming in the hills and uplands changed very
little, such variation as there was being chiefly due to changes
in the quantities of feeding stuffs used. The general improvement in the efficiency of the use of farm resources really

arose from the increase in the value of the output, especially in the price of wool in 1952, rather than in increases in the physical quantities produced. The period was also one of rapid inflation which caused marked changes in farm valuations, particularly of livestock, and these changes were not proportionate to change in the actual numbers of livestock.

The relative efficiency of high-land and lowland farms in the return gained from their use of resources is closer together than was first thought if the amount of Government help given in direct and indirect subsidies is deducted. The index of relative efficiency, with an adjustment for Government subsidies and grants, rose to 92 in the year 1953 for the hills and uplands as compared with 100 per cent for lowland farms. It is probable that the agriculture of the hills and uplands has improved its relative position even further since 1953 due to the advent of the free market. The market prices of mutton, lamb and beef have been close to, or above, the guaranteed prices for these products for most of the time until recently, so that hill and upland farmers to whom these products are important, have been drawing on Government funds to a much smaller extent than their lowland compatriots who, with their emphasis on cereals, milk and bacon, have produced goods which have continued to receive high subsidies in recent years.

Therefore, although the efficiency of use of resources on hill and upland farms is below that of the lowlands, it looks relatively better when the cloak of subsidies is removed. On the basis of this background information, there is at least some encouragement for a critical look into ways and means of improving the agricultural land use of our high ground.

Physical improvements

The uncultivated hill land of Great Britain can best be described as high moorland. The studies of grassland type areas involved in the Grassland Survey of Great Britain made in 1939 suggest that this high moorland is made up of five main vegetative groups: bracken, fescue, nardus, molinia and heather. The soils concerned fall into two chief types

—lighter, drier soils with very good natural drainage, and some heavier soils with poor natural drainage. Any one or several of these vegetative types may form the rough grazings which are the greater part of the acreage of many hill sheep farms but they are a smaller part of the total area of upland farms as these lie on the fringes of the hill country proper.

The soils of these rough grazings are normally very acid, needing large dressings of lime before their productivity can be increased. They are also heavily deficient in phosphates but usually have a relatively high organic matter. Potash is also short except on land heavily covered with bracken. The main object in reclamation of land of this character is to clear away and replace by better species the natural or existing vegetation, whether it be scrub, bracken or grass. At the same time, the soil must become a better environment for new and improved species of plants. Without this second step there is a quick relapse to the original state.

From the many experiments made during the Stapledon era, both by the Welsh Plant Breeding Station and by individual hill farmers who experimented on their own initiative, it was found to be important to take a number of progressive steps in land improvement according to the difficulties of the land in question. It was not simply a choice between full-scale ploughing and reseeding or no action at all. Two other possibilities were found to be effective. The first of these was the mere application of fertilisers on the areas of land where it was impossible to use cultivating machinery of any type. The second method involved the use of surface cultivators and fertilisers on suitable rough land, with or without the sowing of a seeds mixture. The orthodox method used for the land 'in better heart' and much easier to cultivate was, of course, full ploughing, fertilising and reseeding.

In relation to the economics of land improvement the advantage of using fertilisers only is that the productivity of the natural pasture is very slowly improved and, therefore, the farmer is able to increase gradually his expenditure on fertilisers and on extra livestock to graze the improved sward. This method of improvement is important, therefore, to the man who must, in practice, increase his expenditure slowly because the extra capital has to come from his small savings or out of his current income.

The second method, which is rather quicker in its results than the use of fertilisers alone, involves the surface cultivation of the moorland with dressings of fertilisers with or without sowing of a seeds mixture. The degree of improvement is rather slower and smaller than that obtained by the use of the plough but again the capital outlay is less than that needed with ploughing and reseeding where a big increase in the number of livestock is soon needed. On the other hand, a disadvantage of this second method is that the original sward is not killed so that there is a fairly quick reversion back towards its original state unless heavy grazing and constant attempts to keep the higher plane of fertility and productivity are made. Professor Ellison has suggested that much more use could be made of this method, not only on land where the plough cannot be used but also as a form of pre-treatment in earlier years so that a good job can be made of later complete ploughing and reseeding.[1]

The cultivation, application of fertilisers and reseeding of moorland involves a most violent change to hitherto uncultivated land, and though accompanied by relatively heavy costs, is often followed by spectacular improvements. There are variants of the method. For example, sometimes a pioneer crop, such as a mixture of rape and turnips for 'feeding off' with sheep, is used before the grass seed is sown. On land with an inherently higher fertility, pioneer crops, used to build up soil fertility, are sometimes followed by corn or root crops before reseeding to a long-term ley. Finally, the reseeding is very often made directly, either with or without a cover crop.

Though the results of this latter method are often dramatic, heavy costs are involved, particularly if it is necessary to build up fertility with pioneer crops before a very much better sward can be established and maintained. Heavy and increasing costs are involved immediately because of the necessity for higher stocking to consume the growth thrown

[1] Ellison, W., *Marginal Land in Britain*, Geoffrey Bles, 1953.

up by new and vigorous grass and clover species. Very often, additional improvements such as improved roads, fencing, and water supplies have to be incurred in order to make the improvement worth while. Lastly, the job is not 'a once and for all' job. On a farm which is situated at the edge of the moorland, the reclamation of new pieces of land involves a farmer in a repetition of the job probably at least once in every ten years. This means that the farm and farmer must be geared to this higher level of land cultivation; the rhythm must not be seriously broken or quick reversion will occur. Much will depend on the quality of the initial ploughing and discing. If this is done well with the original sward destroyed or effectively buried, the new grass and clover or other crops can grow away without severe competition from indigenous species.

The increase in productivity that can be obtained from the edges of the more suitable areas of moorland by ploughing and reseeding them to temporary pastures has been estimated by Stapledon and Ellison (two authorities on this type of problem) to be roughly four times that of the original vegetation. This is only an average figure. There is, of course, wide variation from district to district. This type of estimate has been obtained from studies of the live weight increase of animals raised on the pastures before and after improvement. The increase in production is not a sharp initial increase and then a constant productivity at around four times the original level. The increase is actually very much greater than four times during the early years but it then falls away, and it is only over a period of eight to ten years that such a fourfold increase occurs.

The economics of hill improvement

It is, then, technically possible to get quite marked increases in the physical productivity of selected pieces of uncultivated moorland. The additional information necessary relates to the costs and returns obtainable in farming the reclaimed land. Costs vary tremendously according to the methods of improvement used and particularly whether the method chosen has been one showing an immediate return or a smaller increase over a longer period by cheaper methods such as the application of fertilisers only. The level of cost is influenced by whether or not a good initial job is done and whether quite rapid renewal and further expense is involved once the improvement cycle has been started. The returns obtained depend, of course, on how the farmer uses the increased quantity and quality of grass and clover and whether or not the livestock into which he converts it are relatively high- or low-priced. Grass once grown can be turned into mutton or lamb, beef or veal or milk. The monetary return will be very different in each of these cases. There is, in addition, another important loss in that some of the new grass will be wasted by being under-grazed at certain times or poorly converted into winter feed as hay or silage.

Many surveys carried out on the problems and possibilities of hill and upland farming in the 1930's and since World War II have shown a low level of output from these types of holdings, together with a need for improvement in other physical and social facilities such as roads, water supplies, fences, houses and farm buildings. It has often been stressed in the reports of such surveys that the improvement of facilities of this kind is important not only to enable an increase in farm production to become possible but even to maintain production at its present level. In other words, a case for State help has often been suggested, not only to increase farm production but also in order to keep certain hill holdings actually in human occupation. This only reflects the amalgam of physical, economic and social problems which are involved whenever one looks at the problems of hill and upland agriculture.

The comprehensive nature of the problem was recognised in the framing of the Hill Farming Act of 1946, followed by the Livestock Rearing Act of 1951, where provision was made for grant aid to the improvement of most facilities to be found on a general high-land farm. It is basic to the 1951 Act that a decision to give a 50 per cent grant from Government funds towards the cost of the comprehensive improvement of a farm is only made if there is a prospect of the holding becoming an economic unit after the work of rehabilitation has been carried out.

Here is a dilemma. In many cases increases in the incomes of farms can be obtained most successfully and most quickly by putting new capital into purely husbandry improvements. But fixed equipment and living conditions are relatively so bad on many of these farms that longer-term improvements must be made and encouraged. The difficulty is that improvements in the fixed farming structure and in social improvements take a long time to show their effects in increased farm income. It is, therefore, very difficult to judge by any material yardstick whether or not they have been worth while.

Behind these Acts also lies the hope that some extra Government assistance to high-land farms would be reflected in increased supplies of meat animals. It should be remembered that this was a very important topic just before 1951 because of the smallness of the British meat ration. It was also realised that the farms on our high land suffer from inflexibility of land use. There are only certain products that the land and farms are able to produce. In addition, these farms do not normally produce end products for which there are guaranteed markets and prices. This is particularly true for the farms which produce mainly store sheep and cattle. Apart from wool, the incomes of these farmers are largely, though indirectly, determined by the ultimate profit to be obtained from the end products, i.e. beef and mutton. If the relative profitability of end products such as meat is low, then the lowland farmer will concentrate on arable and cash cropping and the demand for store animals will decline. This relative depression will seep back to the hill farm, leading to depressed standards of living there together with attempts to change the type of farm production. It is because of this relative depression in sheep and cattle prices for so many years that some of the farms in Britain's hill areas have moved into milk production, even though they have a relative disadvantage in its production as compared with farms on the lowlands.

The decision to offer Government funds for selected schemes of comprehensive farm improvement to the peculiar

class of farm to be found in the high lands of Great Britain
was greatly strengthened by the results of a special survey
made of such land and farms in the autumn of 1949. This
survey was carried out under the auspices of the Agricultural
Research Council and was directed by Professor Ellison of
the University College of Wales, Aberystwyth, and Dr. Boyd,
statistician at the Soil Science Research Station at Rotham-
sted. During the survey, estimates were made of the cost
of farm improvement and the likely returns accruing from
them. As we are particularly interested in the problem of
deciding where it is most worth while for the community
as a whole to invest its capital in terms of increased resources
in land in agriculture, it is important to carefully examine
this survey and its results. [1,2] It is needed as a basis for the
later examination of other types of land improvement on
areas in the lowlands. At the same time, the marginal costs
and returns involved in hill improvements may be valuable
in setting a top limit to the national cost of taking land from
agriculture for non-agricultural purposes as it will show the
maximum expense involved in replacing the food now grown
on the land zoned for future urban growth.

The area of land surveyed by Ellison and Boyd lay within
the one-quarter of the land surface of Britain known as
livestock rearing land. The definition of it embodied in the
Livestock Rearing Act of 1951 is interesting and important.
It consists of 'land situated in an area consisting predominantly of mountains, hills or heath, being land which is, or
by improvement could be made, suitable for use for the
breeding, rearing and maintenance of sheep or cattle but not
for the carrying on, to any material extent, of dairy farming,
the production to any material extent of fat sheep or fat
cattle or the production of crops in quantity materially
greater than that necessary to feed the number of sheep or
cattle capable of being maintained on the land.' Land of this
character can be found in the counties of Cheshire, Cornwall,

[1] Ellison, W., *Marginal Land in Britain*, Geoffrey Bles, 1953.
[2] Boyd, D. A., and Ellison, W., 'Possibilities of Marginal Land Reclamation: Some Results of a Survey in England and Wales,' *Journal of the Royal
Agricultural Society of England*, **113**, 1952, pp. 26–43.

Cumberland, Derby, Devon, Durham, Hereford, Lancaster, Northumberland, Shropshire, Somerset, Stafford, Westmorland, Worcester, and York (North and West Riding) in England, together with all counties in Wales (except Anglesey but including Monmouth), and all counties in Scotland.

The questions which the survey tried to answer were:

(1) What is the extent of the marginal areas of the hills and uplands falling within this definition?

(2) What would be the cost of improving and rehabilitating the holdings involved over a period of about six years in order to obtain greater and more efficient production?

(3) What sort of increase in output could be expected during the same period, particularly in terms of store cattle and sheep, and what would be the value of this increase compared with its likely cost?

The survey work involved the random selection of farms of, broadly, the livestock rearing type in three main regions in Northern and South-West England and in Wales.

The surveyors visited the farms selected in order to consider what improvements were desirable on each farm as judged as a business unit. In addition, the extent to which improvement in farm-houses and buildings, roads and services were required was recorded.

The survey was designed to obtain information about a possible six-year programme of improved cropping and stock production on each farm and also to record what was necessary for the general rehabilitation of the holding as a place on which to live as well as to work. The average size of the farm surveyed was about 120 acres, with about two-thirds of this area under crops and grass and the remainder under rough grazing. The area of rough grazing varied tremendously from farm to farm, rising to nearly half of the total in the north of England, and falling to less than one-fifth on farms in East Wales and along the Welsh border country.

Estimates for the actual productivity of the various categories of land on the farms studied, and how it would increase because of the specified improvements suggested, were made in the form of yields of starch equivalent per acre per annum. The recommendations of the surveyors varied but, in general, amounted to suggestions of greater use of lime and fertiliser on most of the land, and improvement of the grassland together with certain parts of the rough grazing, by means of either manurial treatment or ploughing up and reseeding.

The cost of improvement was estimated on the basis of an initial charge, together with the subsequent cost of maintenance during the remaining years of the six-year period. They were expressed in terms of average cost per acre for the whole farm including any rough grazing land. The costs involved covered things such as cultivations, applications of lime and fertilisers, draining and fencing, together with added expenditure on labour, machinery and more livestock. In addition, as part of the rehabilitation of the farm, estimates were made of the cost of repairing and rebuilding farmhouses, farm buildings and farm roads, together with any extra new capital expenditure such as new cottages for additional farm workers and additional equipment for livestock, and the supply of water and of electricity to the farm.

The total capital cost per acre of marginal land improvement and rehabilitation was finally obtained (Table 12). The average expenditure was just over £32 an acre on land and farm improvements extending over a six-year period.

It was pointed out by Ellison and Boyd that this £32 an acre over-represented the amount of new capital which the occupier had had to find immediately. Many of the improvements were to be spread over six years and extra income would come in to recoup some of the costs before the end of this period. In addition, many costs would be grant-aided under the Hill Farming Act and under existing grants such as those for drainage and installing water supplies. Because of recoupment of capital through extra income and grant-aiding, it was felt that the requirements of new capital by the farmer or landlord would be reduced to £16 or £17 over a six-year period, including a capital sum of £3 per acre for new breeding stock.

Table 12
THE CAPITAL COST OF MARGINAL LAND IMPROVEMENT AND
REHABILITATION IN ENGLAND AND WALES IN THE LATE 1940'S*

	£ per acre	
Land Improvement:		
Cultivations and seeds	4·1	
Lime and fertilisers	3·4	
Drainage	2·5	
Fencing	0·9	
Total		10·9
Rehabilitation:		
Farm-houses	1·9	
Farm buildings	8·2	
Farm roads	2·3	
Cottages	1·3	
Water supply	3·0	
Sheep dipping, troughs, shelter belts, etc.	0·7	
Total		17·4
Machinery		1·0
Total of Land Improvement and Rehabilitation		29·3
Breeding stock		3·0
TOTAL		32·3

* Ellison, W., *Marginal Land in Britain*, Geoffrey Bles, London, 1953, Table 21, p. 160.

The average annual cost per acre for carrying out these various improvements is of course quite difficult to decide. In Table 13 the authors' breakdown of estimated annual cost is shown, from which they conclude that the total annual costs per acre would be roughly £5 per acre. The cost to the farmer would, they thought, not be much above £4 per acre because of existing grants under the Hill Farming Act and the value of betterment.

The investigators estimated that returns on the investment over the six-year period should run at approximately £4·2 per acre per year. This estimate was based on the assumption that most of the increased starch equivalent produced would be sold off in the form of sheep and cattle, with a small amount going to pigs and poultry. At the time of the report the value of livestock and livestock products, allowing for

Table 13

THE ANNUAL UNSUBSIDISED COST PER ACRE OF MARGINAL LAND
IMPROVEMENT AS ESTIMATED BY ELLISON AND BOYD*

	£ per acre
Cost of cultivations and manures spread over 6 years....	1·90
Cost of drainage and fencing depreciated at 5 per cent..	0·17
Cost of rehabilitation depreciated at 3½ per cent	0·61
Cost of machinery depreciated at 12½ per cent..........	0·12
Allowance for cost of extra labour for stock............	0·25
Allowance for cost of additional stock................	0·40
Total	3·45
Interest on £32·3 of Capital at 4 per cent..............	1·29
Total annual cost...............................	4·74

* Ellison, W., *Marginal Land in Britain*, Geoffrey Bles, London, 1953,
Table 22, p. 162.

some milk produced, was equivalent to £1 per hundredweight
of starch equivalent produced.

On the basis of this comparison, i.e. a postulated annual
receipt of £4·2 per acre as against an estimated annual cost
to the farmer of roughly the same amount, it was suggested
that special State aid should be given to comprehensive farm
improvements of this type. At the total cost of improvements
within the farm of £32 per acre to an owner-occupier who is
responsible for all the improvements postulated, a grant of
50 per cent would reduce this capital outlay to between £16
and £17 per acre. On this lower level of capital outlay to the
private farmer it was thought likely that the receipts would
exceed the real costs, leaving the farmer with a return margin
of just over £1 per acre per year. On this basis it was expected
that individual farmers and owners would be prepared to put
part of their own money forward in order to get 50 per cent
grants.

On the basis of this survey the investigators concluded
that there was approximately 5,000,000 acres of the particular
class of upland livestock rearing farms suitable for improvement in the United Kingdom, of which 3,750,000 acres could
be markedly improved in this way and to this extent.

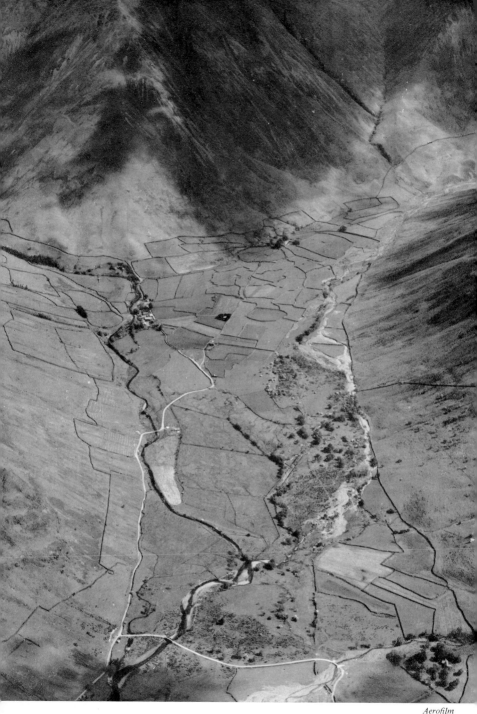

Aerofilm

In the hill lands of west and north Britain, agricultural cultivation uses only the valley bottoms and the less severe slopes. The margins of cultivation and of human residence are very clear cut. Wasdale Head, Cumberland.

A later survey and analysis by the same team of investigators was made in 1953 and 1954 and published in late 1955.[1] In the intervening period of time the Livestock Rearing Act of 1951 had been brought into operation which, together with the Hill Farming Act, now gave substantial grants and subsidies to those farming hill and upland farms where the rearing of cattle and sheep were the major activities. The new survey, which used the same basic pattern of investigation as the first one, attempted to compare the results of grant aid received by chosen farms under these two Acts with the progress of other but similar farms which had received no such help.

The important results for us at this stage are the level of returns in relation to costs which were to be expected and which actually occurred. The results of the first survey suggested that there would be little or no profit margins for the upland farmer on a system of comprehensive improvement, though he should cover his costs. To give him an incentive, grants rising to 50 per cent have been made by the Government on comprehensive farm improvements, both to land and to living conditions and permanent farm equipment under the 1951 Livestock Rearing Act. On these it has been suggested by the earlier survey that, though the total return on the new social and private capital investment might be only about 3 to 5 per cent, the private farmer should be able to obtain a net return of not less than 10 per cent after payment of interest charges on both the farm and landowners' capital.

The capital required for each acre of land thought capable of being improved was estimated at £32. But this covers only

[1] Ellison, W., Boyd, D. A., and Church, B. M., 'The Progress of Improvement on Upland and Hill Farms in England and Wales,' *Journal of the Royal Agricultural Society of England*, **116**, 1955, pp. 34–49.

A recent and important new use of land is the opencast working of mineral deposits. Views like these are now customary in the ironstone areas of Northants, though they are temporary because of the compulsory restoration of the land, usually to agriculture, after the mineral has been taken out. Cranford Surface Working—
Northants.

Aerofilm

F

the extra capital required within the farm. Rather less than half of this amount would be spent on improvements to the land itself in the form of additional cultivations, manuring, draining and fencing. Most of the remainder would be needed for improvements still within the farm, of buildings, cottages, farm roads and physical services like piped water and electricity. This £32 would, then, be the total capital commitments of the landlord and tenant combined or of the owner-occupier (except that the presence of special Government grants removes some of the incidence of the cost away from the farmer to the State).

To make many of the improvements possible and all of them long lasting, extra capital investment would be involved in things outside the confines or control of the individual farm. For example, the Ellison and Boyd survey suggested that an extra £4 per acre of improvable land would be needed to be spent on minor roads off the farm which are inadequately maintained at the present time. The bringing in of main water supplies and of grid electricity, the extra costs of deliveries of goods and services because of long distances and poor roads, the long distance transport of children to school—these and others are expenses borne by the State which are above those incurred by lowland rural areas. In terms of both private and State capital, therefore, the figure is considerably higher than £32 per improvable acre, and to cover some of these major 'off the farm' costs the total has been raised to £40 as the amount of capital likely to be involved in the permanent improvement of the hills and uplands. As a result of such investment, the surveyors felt that an increase of 70 per cent above the present output of the land would be achieved.

The second survey throws some light on what has actually occurred, though much more time and research and better methods of evaluation are needed to give the long-term and correct results. The investment of new capital was obviously proceeding more slowly than expected and farmers were using it on types of improvement which showed quicker returns than those expected by the investigators. In all, the return being obtained on the total social and private capital

was only at the level expected, that is, of 3 to 5 per cent, but
the individual farmer, on his much smaller capital investment,
was receiving a reasonable return of 10 to 12 per cent.

The upper limit to the cost of food replacement

These 'before and after' surveys of improvement possibilities in the hills and uplands are valuable to the argument in
this book because from them the upper limits to the cost of
replacing the food now being produced on farm land earmarked for urban development can be obtained.

The calculation for the 1949 period is thus:

£ *per acre*

Average 'net' agricultural output of the land earmarked for urban growth in England and Wales in
1949–50, was .. .. 28·7

Average 'net' agricultural output of improvable
uplands in 1949–50 was .. .. 7·8

Increased by 70 per cent, as estimated to be practicable, gives .. .. 13·3

It will therefore take the increased output from:

$$\frac{28·7}{13·3 - 7·8} =$$ 5·2 acres of improved uplands to compen-
sate for each acre lost to urban growth.

Extra capital, social and private, needed to secure and
maintain this increased production has been estimated at
£40 per acre.

Therefore the food replacement capital cost for each
urbanised acre is:

$$5·2 \times 40 = £208 \text{ in } 1949–50.$$

This calculation can be made for a later date, assuming that
costs of farm improvement have increased in line with the
prices of other things in the economy; thus:

£ *per acre*

Average net agricultural output of the agricultural
land zoned for urban growth in 1955–6 was .. 41·0

Average net agricultural output of improvable uplands in 1955–6 was .. .. 9·0

This increased by 70 per cent, as considered
possible .. .. 15·3

It would therefore take the increased output from:

$$\frac{41}{15\cdot3 - 9\cdot0} = \text{6·5 acres of improvable upland to compensate for each acre lost to urban growth.}$$

The extra capital, social and private, needed to secure and maintain this increased level of output was estimated, in 1949–50, to be £40 per acre.

At this figure, the upper limit of the food replacement capital cost for each urbanised acre would be:

$$£40 \times 6\cdot5 = £260.$$

But the costs of improvements in the uplands must have been higher in 1955–6 than they were in 1949–50. Adjusting for changes in the level of wholesale prices, the probable capital cost rises to £54 and the food replacement figure to £351.

From this discussion of the technical and economic possibilities of land improvement at the margin of cultivation we can see the upper limit to the possibilities of bringing in new or improved land to replace land being taken by other uses. At this limit, this democratic country, through its elected representatives in Parliament, has encouraged, by a system of grant-aid and subsidies, improvements in farm output which are costing an equivalent of £208 per urbanised acre at 1949–50 levels, and £351 at 1955–6 levels. Thus the replacement of each £41 of net farm output that is abandoned when a lowland acre is taken over for urban purposes can and does involve large capital investment sums of around £350.

The increase as between 1949 and 1956 in the size of the necessary capital investment in the hills and uplands to replace the annual money value of each acre of lowland earmarked for planned urbanisation is due to two main causes. The major one is the relative increase in the value of the agricultural output of the better lowland over the produce from upland farms between these years. The other cause is the rise in the cost of making capital improvements to hill farms and hill land.

These comparisons are rough and are only designed to show relationships between the costs and returns of various forms of agricultural land saving and land spending. Obviously, the types of farm products coming off the land zoned for urban growth in the lowlands and those produced on high-land farms are very different. Milk, market-garden crops and cash arable products like cereals and sugar beet satisfy different needs than the store cattle and sheep which come from the hills. Nevertheless, the difficulty of producing hill-farming products, as shown in the use of capital, is reflected by this food replacement type of analysis.

The social problems of the hills

There are, however, complicated and interrelated social problems to the rehabilitation of our hill areas which are not completely covered by stating a gross total of new investment capital. There are the difficulties of growing crops and livestock and of making a good living within the individual farm, but, in addition, there is the problem of maintaining and improving the attributes of such isolated and climatically difficult areas so that enough people will accept them as worth-while places in which to live and bring up children.

In the implementation of permanent improvements in the agriculture of such areas, only partial control lies within the agricultural industry. The earnings of landowners, the profits of farmers and the wages paid to farm workers are internal matters for agriculture. Yet, living conditions for these people lie partly outside the control of the individual farmer or landlord. Certainly, new cottages may be built on the farm and old ones modernised and in some cases water and electricity from private installations can be, and are being, provided. But there remain a variety of factors like frequency of bus service, distance to a school, shop or village hall, over which the individual farmer has little control.

It is foolish to expect or insist on the complete provision of public services and social amenities throughout the true hill farming areas of this country, as the population which the areas can carry, unless there are activities complementary to agriculture, is too small and too scattered to justify the cost. It is, therefore, important that people in these areas should be able to earn an income sufficiently high and steady to enable them to improve their own living conditions and to use public and private means of access to their houses or farms. This suggests that public expenditure on isolated schemes of improvement to farms and farm cottages in such districts can be justified, even though that expenditure may be divorced from any radical improvement to general social conditions. It is much more economical for the community to concentrate its public services in areas of slightly greater population or at only one or two key points instead of trying to take them to all the isolated dwellings which are present in mountainous country. It is cheaper and, possibly, psychologically better to make it possible for the few individuals which the community needs in these areas, in order to use the land for its most economic purpose, to earn a sum large enough to provide their own means of getting to and from their farms and homes.

This really is an argument for the subsidisation of individuals rather than to merely subsidise the land and farms. There is no basic illogicality in the argument that in the list of farm improvements to which Government grants are made, items designed to improve the mobility of the farmer, his men and their wives and children should be included. These are items like cars, vans and vehicles with four-wheel drive which can handle the rough, poor roads. It might be far cheaper and better to subsidise such things than to attempt to lay out much more capital in improving all roads, and in bringing publicly provided social and physical services to the door of each house.

In the uplands bordering the hills a different kind of curative treatment is needed. These areas have a greater density of population than in the hills and often an agricultural potential that has been under-exploited because of deficiencies in living conditions. Among these, poor housing and lack of piped water and electricity are great drawbacks to country life in the eyes of most people, but inadequate sanitation, scattered schools and infrequent bus services, and isolation from shops or entertainment are added disadvantages in the eyes of many families and individuals. The provision of some of these facilities is a matter for local private enterprise, but local and central Government bodies, as well as public Boards, are concerned in supplying four of the more important deficiencies—housing, schools, piped water and electricity. The total of the deficiencies, even for these four items, over the countryside as a whole is so great that it will be a very long time before there is enough capital available to raise all rural areas to a uniformly high standard. Therefore, in the hills and uplands, as between farms, some sort of discrimination in the placement of social capital seems to be required.[1]

Therefore, in looking at the opportunities for new land in the hills proper, it should be realised that returns on capital and in personal incomes must be especially high to be satisfactory over a long period of time. This is because people living in these areas need to buy many of the services which in other more fortunate parts of the country are provided by the community in general. In the lower and more thickly populated regions of the uplands, such as in Central Wales, parts of the Welsh border, North Devon, and in parts of the Pennines and Cheviot Hills, individual farmers and their families will possibly be satisfied with lower returns on their capital and lower personal incomes. But this is true only if the social and physical fabric of their part of the countryside is improved in line with the general improvements in living conditions being made throughout the towns and easily accessible lowland rural areas. The physical and economic difficulties of doing this are great, and possibly improvements should first be made in those areas where only one or a few deficiencies remain to be alleviated or where a major injection of public capital will enable the agricultural potential of the area to be realised. This choice of areas and of projects for improvement can best be done by close co-operation between County Agricultural and Planning Committees.

At this juncture all that should be said is that there are heavy social costs to be added to those of the private

[1] Wibberley, G. P., 'Some Aspects of Problem Rural Areas in Britain,' *The Geographical Journal*, **120**, March 1954, pp. 43–58.

landowner and farmer in the task of gaining 'new' land for food production in the hills and uplands. But, surely, both the costs to the private farmer and to the community in providing better social and physical services will be lighter if 'new' land is sought in the lowlands, either by the reclamation of odd pieces of land which are still poorly used there or by further intensification of the land already in farming use? It is to these matters that we turn our attention in the next chapter.

Chapter 9 New Land—From the Lowlands?

I T may seem curious to suggest that in such a thickly populated and long settled country as Britain there are still appreciable areas of land in the lowlands which could be developed for agricultural use. Surely all the good land has long ago been reclaimed and organised into farms? The sharp rise in the population of this country in the past two centuries, the increasing demand for food, with the increased purchasing power of all families, and the change over to foods like meat, which need large areas of land for their efficient production, suggest that England would long ago have absorbed all available land into agricultural and urban uses. Yet this is not the visual impression gained by the visitor from the city and from abroad who travels the length and breadth of the countryside and compares what he or she sees with the position in other parts of the world with population densities of like magnitude.

The reasons for this seemingly surprising lack of intensive food production in the British countryside are clear-cut and unique. The most important has been the lack of dependence on home land resources for the total food supply of the country over the past century. In the 1930's the home produced portion of total food supplies was roughly 40 per cent of the total, by value. Targets and achievements since then have raised it to more than 50 per cent. In addition, the fact of a wide variety of food being available from overseas has diverted British agriculture into the production of those commodities in which it has a comparative advantage like milk, eggs and sheep, or into the growing of crops or raising of livestock specially encouraged by Government support, such as wheat, barley and oats, pigs and beef cattle. Some of these products can be produced most economically on extensive systems, using grass produced from permanent pastures and grass leys but others are often produced with the help of imported feeding stuffs. This encourages the creation of factory-type systems of food production on farms side by side with an extensive use of the land resources of such farms.

To these economic and political reasons can be added the presence of a physical farming structure which, though it has many faults and inefficiencies, is yet much more adaptable to large-scale production than its counterpart in most European countries where agricultural self-sufficiency is the usual goal. More than 80 per cent of the total agricultural area of the United Kingdom was, in 1950, being farmed in holdings of above 45 acres in extent. The figure for France was 60 per cent and for our industrial competitor, Western Germany, only just over 30 per cent. Not being constrained to produce the total food needs of the existing population, the British farmer has been able to adapt his systems of farming to a relatively high production of food of high value from a fairly unrestricted area of land. Production has, however, had to be geared to the presence of relatively few farm workers because of their high cost. This is due to the competition of the large number of non-farming jobs often situated close to farming areas. Basically, then, the farming pattern is designed to use less labour than its European counterparts.

It is not always realised by the ordinary traveller in the British countryside that its dominant landscape pattern— that of the field of varied size and shape separated by the hedgerows and interspersed with the copse—is being maintained because of a fundamental decision in British farm practice. It is the decision to make our farm livestock travel to and collect most of their own food. We in Britain make our animals work for their own keep. They are turned out of buildings as much as possible, persuaded along lanes, enticed through gateways and kept within and on smallish areas of land mainly by a form of controlled vegetation, known as the 'quick' or hawthorn hedge. As much as possible of their food is grown to be eaten in the same place. This is true of important foods like grass leys and less important ones such as kale, turnips and swedes for folding off. Even the fields in arable cultivation, from which crops are sold for cash or else hand-fed to animals in their winter quarters, are, in most areas, surrounded by hedges or fences because, in their turn in the rotation of crops, they will have animals grazing on them.

One can see in this, therefore, a major reason for the contrast in the rural scenery of the lowlands of much of the Continent to that of the lowlands of Britain. In most other European countries the larger proportion of the food that each farm animal eats is taken to it. Even if the continental cow or sheep is allowed to graze, it is often 'fenced in' as it were, by the radius of its tethering rope or by the eternal vigilance of the old peasant grandmother or small child who tends these moments of relative liberty for the few cows or a small flock of sheep.

In these parts of other countries where human labour is valued at so much less than in Britain, there is then no need for stock-proof fences or hedges. Only boundary marks are necessary between the different occupiers and owners of the vast stretches of open countryside. Even the shade of the odd tree or copse is not so important as farm animals remain indoors through much of the hot summer day.

Many people think we have a lot to learn about efficient land use from the European countries and they are often particularly impressed with the lack of waste land in shaws or hedges, or under single trees, the handcutting of the grass on the roadside verges and the carrying of it to the villages for the feeding of cattle housed there. This is something which we should not admire but rather regret, as the time and energy of human beings are surely more important and more worth while husbanding than those of animals. The carrying, for example, of a large amount of green cut grass by human beings is a form of very burdensome water carrying. It is well worth while 'wasting' some land if more and better food can be produced cheaply and with less human drudgery.

Our field and hedge pattern will, therefore, always give the impression that there is considerable waste of land in the lowlands of Britain. The fact that the major use of our land is the growing of grass, either in a permanent form or as mixtures of temporary grass and clover species, again gives the illusion of low productivity. It is very difficult to convince the ordinary city dweller that a good grass field can produce more food than many arable crops.

The nation has the problem of deciding whether it should use any increases in its relatively scarce and expensive resources on either bringing in more land into the national farm, intensifying the use of the land already under cultivation, or leaving the national farm as it is and using the extra resources in some other employment where the added returns to extra investment would be greater than in agriculture. Here we need to measure the extra returns to be received on spending £100 on bringing in more land into cultivation, as compared with the return to be obtained from its investment on more intensive uses of existing land; and both being compared with the market rates of interest on such capital when used elsewhere in the economy. Obviously, decisions of this sort are relative in nature because so many of the components of cost and returns can change so quickly in value. To an individual farmer the difficult question is to decide when and where it is worth while spending capital on increasing the land area of a holding rather than putting it to other uses, such as improved farm buildings, better and more machinery, more fertilisers or hiring more or better farm workers.

We are here faced with the two margins of cultivation— the extensive and the intensive. If a farmer has access to as much land as he wants but that land varies in fertility, he will farm an area of land down to that quality where the return he gets from the last acre only just covers the capital and labour he spends on it but leaves no reward to the land itself. This last acre of land of low quality is said to be at the *extensive* margin of cultivation and is worth no rent because its product is only just sufficient to cover the cost of the other factors of production which have had to be used on it.

If, however, a man has only a limited area of land he can profitably intensify his agricultural production to that point where the last pound he spends on capital or labour used on this fixed area of land is just covered by the extra product obtained. The fixed area of land is then being farmed up to the *intensive* margin. If this man has made available to him an extra area of land which is unreclaimed he is really faced with a decision between these two margins. He has to decide whether he should use his capital and labour resources on bringing in some more land into his farm or whether it would be better for him to neglect the unreclaimed land and use his resources on intensifying production from the land he already has in full farming use.

Studies by J. O. Jones[1] suggest that at present levels of rent it would pay farmers in this country to use *more* land with existing labour and capital. They have been under-paying for their land. He found that for the early 1950's the economic rent of land of average quality appeared to be about £4$\frac{1}{2}$ to £5 per acre, a figure so much higher than actual rents being paid that it was thought that a 100 per cent increase in average rents would still leave a reasonable return to land where farmers adjusted their farming systems so as to use their land more intensively and efficiently. He also could not discover any major difference in the efficiency with which land was being used as between small farms under 45 acres in size and those above this level.

One suggestion is, therefore, that there are worth-while opportunities for increasing agricultural production by the more intensive use of the land already inside farm boundaries; in other words, that very few British farmers, even on the lowlands, are farming right up to the intensive margin on the land they hold. But before looking critically at the various ways in which the use of farm land can be intensified, what of the unused parts of the lowlands? Are they large in area and significant in their possibilities for economic reclamation? On the basis of estimates made by Professor Ellison,[2] the Natural Resources (Technical) Committee[3] made the

[1] Jones, J. O., 'The Productivity of Major Factors in British Farming I and II,' *The Farm Economist*, Oxford University Press, Vol. VIII, No. 4, 1955, and Vol. VIII, No. 5, 1956.

[2] Ellison, W., *Marginal Land in Britain*, Geoffrey Bles, London, 1953, especially Chapter III.

[3] Natural Resources (Technical) Committee, 'Forestry, Agriculture and Marginal Land. Office of the Lord President of the Council,' H.M.S.O., London, 1957.

statement given in Table 14 as to the amount of low-lying marginal land present in Great Britain:

Table 14
AREA OF MARGINAL LAND ON THE LOWLANDS OF GREAT BRITAIN

	Total area available Million acres	Area thought to be improvable for agricultura purposes Million acres
Poor quality heavy land	0·8	0·25
Poor quality light land................	0·8	0·25
Marshes	0·1	0·1
Small parcels of marginal land on medium and good land	0·25	0·2
Total	1·95	0·8

The total of improvable marginal land was thought to be about 4,100,000 acres, of which 3,250,000 lay in the upland livestock rearing areas and 800,000 in the lowlands.

It is likely that there is available about 1,000,000 acres of unused land in the lowlands which is good potential agricultural land, that is, about one and a half times the area which will pass over to urban uses between 1950 and 1970. The total is put above the 800,000 acres estimate because of the possibilities of accretions of land on certain parts of the coast and the reclamation of derelict woodland which have not been included to a large enough extent in Ellison's estimates.

Let us now look at the possibilities of each major category of potential 'new' land on the lowlands.

New land from the sea

The area of potentially usable foreshore areas and saltings has been estimated at 527,000 acres in England and Wales, the two largest areas being present in the Wash on the east coast and in Morecambe Bay on the west. It is likely that this estimate is considerably on the high side because of doubts as to the usefulness of the very sandy coastal sediments if they were reclaimed.

The economics of the problem involves choosing between

the alternatives of either the large scale and expensive enclosure of a large area of water, as in the 'polder' work of the Dutch in their reclamation of the former Zuider Zee, or the taking in of small areas of marshland over a long period based on the natural processes of accretion. This second method is slow and small in scale but it involves much less capital, and the land reclaimed is of high potential fertility. It is, in fact, the method which, we believe, will continue to be used in Britain, and our studies have been confined to modest reclamation projects of this type.

Table 15
COSTS OF COASTAL RECLAMATION
(Items adjusted to 1955 prices)

Item	Number of cases	Acreage involved	Cost in £ per acre	
			Range	Median
Embankment and sluices......	7	3,557	53–78	65
Creek filling, ditching and drainage	7	3,557	17–45	35
Fencing and water supply	6	2,807	3–17	12
Roads and buildings..........	4	887	14–30	24
Total				136

A simplified picture of the range and structure of costs involved in recent cases of coastal land reclamation are given in Table 15. If the median figures are taken, it can be seen that the essential costs for any reclamation scheme bringing in small areas of accreted coast or estuarine land would be of the order of £112 per acre. Additional expenditure on roads and buildings depends largely on whether the new land is being added to an existing farm or whether it will have to be farmed as a self-contained unit. It will be non-existent or low in the first case as usually small areas added to existing farms can be satisfactorily handled by the existing fixed equipment.

These costs of coastal reclamation are usually spread over a period of fifteen to twenty years because of the need for consolidation of the soil before permanent drainage work is done and because the land is usually suitable only for grazing for a number of years. This means that the heavier costs of arable cultivation can be postponed in the early years though, unfortunately, the higher returns available from arable cropping must also be postponed.

An attempt was made to build up a hypothetical case of coastal reclamation from the information available as this was thought to be more valuable than a mere summary of the case records which were obtained. Against an anticipated capital expenditure of £136 per acre a net return of about £3·5 per acre could be expected for the first ten year whilst the new land is consolidating under grass. When the land is fit for full-scale arable cropping, its high quality enables a net return of about £14 per acre to be earned.

These figures represent the capital costs and returns, net of annual cost, during the early 1950's, with the land being farmed as a self-contained unit. The return earned on capital is approximately $2\frac{1}{2}$ per cent for the first ten years followed by 10 per cent in later years. These two different levels of return are equivalent to $6\frac{1}{2}$ per cent. If deductions are made for grants and subsidies already available to farmers and landlords for certain operations like tile drainage, ditching, fencing and water supply, the capital involved by the owner in the job will drop from £136 to about £114 per acre, giving a return on the investment of $7\frac{1}{2}$ per cent. The capital needed by the individual may be even lower and the rate of return consequently higher if the reclaimed land is joined to an existing farm with fixed equipment, like buildings and roads, which are adequate to farm both the new and the old land. The amount of capital needed can then be as low as £90 per acre to the private individual.

Because of the relatively high value of the agricultural output finally obtained from this type of land reclamation, the capital cost of this method of replacing the value of agricultural output to be lost by planned urban expansion is relatively low. The 'food replacement' figure is £225 per urbanised acre over the lower productivity of the first ten years after reclamation and it falls to £118 when the land is able to be used for full arable cropping.

The evidence suggests that the slow and piecemeal type of land reclamation from the sea is an economic proposition but it is not highly or immediately profitable to the individual. Its long term-nature also makes it risky if a progressive lowering of agricultural prices in future years is thought likely. Fears of this sort and the peculiar difficulty of paying back loans in equal instalments on a capital investment which yields low returns in the early years but higher ones later may be responsible for the lack of active coastal reclamation at the present time. A period of lower interest rates and more flexibility in the terms of repayment of loans could help to increase the practice, particularly if the State improved its grant-aid to this sort of work on the ground that it is a type of land 'winning' which is well worth while in most cases, especially when compared with other types of State aided land improvement schemes.

Land needing drainage

Some areas of land, because of slope or the highly pervious nature of the soil and subsoil, drain naturally. But there are many areas where artificial drainage is valuable in increasing the range of crops that can be grown. There is little evidence, however, in this country, though there is more in Holland, as to the exact optimum water table levels for various crops or systems of cropping on different soils.

The Dutch consider artificial drainage as essential for the arable cropping of clay soils and it is generally accepted as desirable for most of the heavy clay soils in England. Nicholson[1] has estimated these to total 4,000,000 acres, with half of this acreage being in East Anglia. About 500,000 acres of it had been drained by 1941 and there have been large increases since. In addition to such areas of impervious soils, there are the areas suffering from high water tables. These conditions are to be found in the flood plains of rivers and in coastal marshes. When properly drained, as in the Fens, such lands often provide soils of the highest fertility. There is thought to be about 100,000 acres of this type of land in

[1] Nicholson, H. H., *The Principles of Field Drainage*, Cambridge University Press, 2nd Edition, 1953, Chapter XIV, p. 147.

Kent alone and more than 300,000 in eastern and south-eastern England, and only a small part of it is satisfactorily drained.

A large amount of agricultural drainage work, in the form of ditch clearing, mole and tile drainage has been done by farmers since 1941 with the financial and other help of the Ministry of Agriculture. More than 5,000,000 acres are thought to have benefited from ditch clearing whereas more than 1,000,000 acres have been drained by mole ploughs or the laying of tile drains. Yet it is very difficult to know to what extent production from this land has been increased by the work, how often part of the drainage work has had to be repeated and how much more land there is in the countryside which needs artificial drainage.

The costs of drainage vary tremendously from one farm or field to another and they have steadily increased over the years. Costs in 1955 were between £5 and £6 per chain of ditch cleared or about the same amount per acre improved. Mole drainage costs are about the same per acre though it is usually necessary to draw new moles about once every five years and this means an extra annual maintenance charge of about £1 per acre to cover this recurring expenditure. The costs of tile drainage work were averaging £26 per acre in 1955.

It can be suggested, therefore, that on a clay soil a drainage scheme needing both ditching and mole drainage could cost about £12 per acre, with recurrent maintenance costs. With both ditching and tile drainage the total cost would be about £32 per acre and, with adequate ditch maintenance, the life of the tile system is considered to be between forty to fifty years. These are total costs. The costs to the farmer are much less because of Government grants on approved ditching, mole and tile drainage schemes of 50 per cent of the full cost.

The returns from drainage would in all probability result in

(1) higher yields of crops, or longer grazing season, with the same fertiliser use or the ability to use higher fertiliser applications;

(2) easier cultivating and harvesting conditions leading, possibly, to lower costs;

(3) the ability to change from an extensive to an intensive use of land as, for example, the change over from typical Romney Marsh grazing of sheep to an intensive arable system growing wheat, barley, canning peas and potatoes.

In our studies at Wye we have found it impossible to disentangle effectively the benefits and monetary returns due solely to expenditure on drainage. Individual case studies did, however, suggest increases in the yields of arable crops which would pay the drainage costs over relatively few years. Even where the drainage work done involved expenditure of up to £50 per acre, the cost would be paid back relatively quickly if the farming pattern could be changed thereby from the grazing of livestock to intensive arable cash cropping.

The upgrading of poor quality heavy or light land

Throughout the centuries there have been areas of poor and difficult land in the lowlands which have been on the edge of cultivation. Many have only come into agricultural use at times when home agriculture has been particularly prosperous. Others have had their agricultural importance revalued downwards or upwards by changes in the emphasis on particular food products, by changes in the techniques of cultivation or crop growing and by the growing cost of hand labour and its replacement by the machine. The sandy heaths of Sherwood and the New Forests, the heavy clays of East Anglia and the thin chalk slopes and tops of the North and South Downs are examples of such areas. High prices for cereals, new temporary grass and clover leys, the provision of piped water, cheap and mobile systems of milk production, the development of the modern farm tractor and tractor implements (such as the Cambridge roll, the disc harrow and combined seed and fertiliser drill), the development of improved spring varieties of cereals, of better fertiliser practice and scientific weed killing have all combined to up-grade the farming value of many of the so-called poor land areas of the country. It is, in fact, likely that many of these areas would remain in full farming use even if agricultural prices slumped because of the economies achieved through such technical improvements. This would leave the smaller traditional mixed farms on the medium grades of land to take the more severe effects of the depression, due to their relative lack of adaptability.

Some of these so-called poor, thin-soiled areas were brought into cultivation during World War II and then re-equipped for permanent farming in the late 1940's. The South Downs in Sussex are a good example of this spectacular change. Land, which was considered unploughable before 1939 because of its slope, thinness of topsoil, lack of nutrients and lack of knowledge of an adequate rotation system to replace the old four-course rotation with its heavy costs of hand-folded sheep, was ripped up in the emergency to grow more cereals. Much of this initial clearance and ploughing had to be done by the Government Agricultural Committees because local landlords and farmers were either unable or unprepared to tackle it themselves. Gloomy, too, were the warnings of many people about this type of work.

The results have, however, been striking. Crop yields have been good and consistent. New farms have been created, and even dairy farming introduced to the tops of these low hills with adequate fencing and the provision of piped water and electricity. Grass, lucerne and clover leys, adapted to the particular circumstances, have been introduced and such land now changes hands at prices even above those of the long established conventional farms on the lower ground. The large size of these new farms, their good field layout, their new buildings and the ease of economic mechanisation have all combined to raise their value during these days of relatively high cereal prices and shortage of vacant farms.

Much of the capital needed to bring such land into more intensive use was provided during the war-time food production campaign. Although records of it have not been kept in a form whereby the expenditure on particular pieces of land or farms can be accurately identified, it is probable that the returns have been good and relatively cheap in comparison with the heavy costs which would have been involved in building operations on such land and in comparison with the relatively high costs of hill and upland farm improvement.

The agricultural use of common land

The complicated situation in relation to common land has been well documented by the 1958 report of the Royal Commission on Common Land.[1] Great difficulties and doubts arose in the classification and measurement of areas of common land because of problems of definition and of poor and incomplete records. The estimate of the area of common land made by the Commission was 1,505,002 acres in England and Wales, with 1,054,661 acres in England and 450,341 in Wales. The size of this area can be compared with the 3,600,000 acres of urban land in England and Wales. These commons vary tremendously in size.

Table 16

VARIATIONS IN THE SIZE OF COMMONS IN ENGLAND*

Size	Number	Area
Over 5,000 acres	39	383,684
1,000 to 5,000	182	399,433
500 to 1,000	128	95,261
200 to 500	267	87,797
100 to 200	239	35,676
50 to 100	314	22,931
25 to 50	391	14,351
10 to 25	513	8,475
	2,073	1,047,608

* Royal Commission on Common Land 1955–58, H.M.S.O., July 1958, Cmd. 462, Table 1, p. 20.

In addition, there were records of 2,442 extra pieces of common land of less than 10 acres in area, but these only added 7,053 acres to the total. Whereas most of this open land is situated on poor soils in the lowlands and on difficult mountain slopes in the hills and uplands, the Commission found that some areas of common land did lie on land of inherently good quality. Existing uses over all of the English

[1] Royal Commission on Common Land 1955–58, H.M.S.O., July 1958, Cmd. 462.

and Welsh commons were 79 per cent for grazing, only 2 per cent as forest and woodland, 10 per cent as purely amenity and recreation, and 8 per cent as scrub and derelict.

The members of the Commission have suggested a combination of better registration, legislation and improvement schemes in order not only to preserve the existing area of common lands, but to improve facilities for public access to them and to increase their productivity. If their recommendations are acted upon by the Government there is likely to be a somewhat greater agricultural and forest use of some of the areas but it is not likely to be large. On the other hand, the indirect benefits to agriculture and forestry of improved arrangements for public use of common land might be considerable. In this heavily populated country, with its ever-increasing numbers of new houses and motorcars, land to which the general public are allowed full access has a unique value. Its presence is likely to take away from the privately owned and occupied countryside an otherwise heavy pressure of trespass and damage from the wandering town dweller. Where little or no use is at present being made of common land, any pieces which could be incorporated into nearby farms, without necessitating major improvements in the fixed equipment or regular labour and machinery complement of these farms, would probably prove quite economic in an agricultural use.

The reclamation of derelict woodland for agricultural use

Although there are some unusual areas where sizeable areas of land in private occupation are still available for reclamation and where private and State reclamation appears to be economic, such as in the Land's End Peninsula,[1] the problem of reclaiming odd pieces of unused land in the lowlands has been examined in relation to the reclamation of derelict woodlands. In co-operation with the Research Group of the Agricultural Land Service of the Ministry of Agriculture, Fisheries and Food, a detailed study has been

[1] Wibberley, G. P., 'Some Aspects of Problem Rural Areas in Britain,' *The Geographical Journal*, **120**, March 1954, pp. 43–58.

made of the technical and economic possibilities of bringing such land into effective farming use.[1]

The census of woodlands 1947–9 suggested that an area of 584,000 acres existed in England and Wales of unproductive or derelict woodlands, that is, scrub, devastated and felled areas. Much of this land has been classified by the Forestry Commission as uneconomic for forestry management. It is likely therefore to remain derelict and a harbour for pests. Improved methods of site clearance, developed from war-time experience, and the fact that many of the woods lie on soils eminently usable for agriculture suggested that agricultural reclamation might well be worth while in many cases. A pilot survey in the relatively heavily wooded county of Hampshire was therefore conducted on about 1,200 acres of derelict woodland which appeared to be physically suitable for agriculture. Full details of the methods used in site clearance and the costs and returns of the operations are given in the published report, and the findings are very pertinent to the question of 'new' land in the lowlands.

The reclamation of the sites involved the clearance of large tree stumps, of smaller trees and bushes, the removal of roots and small wood from the soil, the collection and disposal of rubbish and the preparation of the site for normal farming operations. The equipment used by the contractors consisted of heavy bulldozers and angledozers, heavy bush ploughs and some explosive for removing tree stumps. Some specially designed lifting combs and under-cutters were also used. Variations, in the type and density of vegetation to be cleared, in soil, slope and weather conditions at clearance time and in the actual method of reclamation adopted, produced a wide range in the costs of doing the whole job—from as little as £24 per acre to upwards of £100 (1954 prices). The net cost to the farmer, because of marginal production grants, ranged from £12 to £88 per acre.

The measurement of the returns gained by the agricultural

[1] Hilton, N. A., Tyler, G. J., and Ward, J. T., 'The Reclamation of Derelict Woodland for Agricultural Use,' Ministry of Agriculture, Fisheries and Food, Agricultural Land Service, Technical Report No. 1.

use of this reclaimed land was made by using the method of farm budgeting discussed and adopted in the studies of alternative sites for new urban development in Chapter 5. Bringing in extra land to a farm involves the farmer in the extra costs of growing crops on that land. These costs may be heavy if the presence of the new land involves the farmer in extra expenditure on his buildings, equipment and labour force. But in many cases the farm already has enough buildings, machinery and regular men to absorb the task of farming a few extra acres. In this latter type of case, therefore, the only extra costs are the variable ones involved in actually growing the particular crop on the piece of new land —the cost of the seed, fertiliser, tractor fuel, oil and maintenance and some extra harvesting expenses, plus interest on the extra working capital involved. The receipts obtained from the reclaimed land were not greatly below those obtained on adjoining land which had been in farming use for a long time, especially if the reclamation had been well done and the new land fully absorbed into the cropping rotation of the whole farm.

Some details of the returns arising from this type of land reclamation are given in Table 17. The returns are net, that is, the gross output less the variable costs incurred. The cases involve those farms where the inclusion of the reclaimed land had not forced the farmers to extend their fixed equipment, to increase their machinery or to add to their regular labour force. They are expressed as a proportion of the total capital cost of the reclamation.

The rate of return to the total capital involved over the fifty cases for which complete details could be obtained ranged from −17 to +82 per cent. The median value was 25 per cent. This is a very substantial figure as it represents the return to the nation on total capital expenditure in the average case of this type of land reclamation. The rate of return on farmers' capital, that is, on the total capital outlay, less Government grants towards the cost of reclamation is, in general, much higher. It ranged from −33 per cent to +164 per cent, with a median value of 42 per cent. Thus, in a little over two years, the average farmer doing this work

Table 17

THE RANGE OF RETURN ON CAPITAL FROM THE RECLAMATION
OF DERELICT WOODLAND*

% Interval	Return on Gross Capital Investment. Frequency	Return on the Net Capital Invested by the Farmer. Frequency
−40 to −1..........	4	4
0 to 19.............	14	5
20 to 39	18	14
40 to 59	11	11
60 to 79	2	9
80 to 99	1	4
Above 100 per cent ..	—	3
Total Number of Cases	50	50

* 'The Reclamation of Derelict Woodland for Agricultural Use,' Table 1—
by permission of the Controller of H.M.S.O.

had been able to cover completely his extra capital costs.
This very high rate of return was not due to exceptionally
high yields from the reclaimed woodland but to the combination of these areas of potential additional land together with
fixed equipment, machinery and regular labour which was
under-utilised. This is a fairly common state of affairs on
British lowland farms because of difficulties in matching
exactly the area of land with the resources, like buildings,
machinery and labour, needed to use it to maximum advantage. So many of these farms could add to their acreage with
benefit.

Further cases of derelict woodland reclamation were
examined in Hampshire where the job of reclamation had
involved substantial changes in farm organisation so that
increases in expenditure on fixed equipment, machinery and/
or regular labour had become necessary. The rates of return
on the total capital cost varied from 12 to 100 per cent,
with a median value of 24 per cent. The return to the capital
invested by the farmer, after receipt of Government grant,
ranged from 15 to 188 per cent with an average of 43 per
cent. The size of these returns is as high as those on the
farms where no major changes in farm organisation had

been involved but the results were influenced by fortuitiously lower costs of reclamation.

The results of this study suggest that it would be economic for many lowland farmers to reclaim isolated areas of derelict woodland if they exist on their holdings. On nine out of every ten of the farms surveyed in Hampshire, the increase in their area of cultivated land obtained in this way had been done at a cost usually well below the estimated capital value of the reclaimed land. In addition, the farmers had shown themselves able to farm this extra land without having to take on extra labour, increase their machinery or fixed equipment or lower their standards of farming. The grant aid available under the Marginal Production Scheme has not been necessary to lift the task above the margin of profitability—it has really acted as an incentive payment to kindle interest in a type of land reclamation which looks, initially, very expensive and difficult.

The restoration to agriculture of land used for opencast mineral working

Throughout this century an increasing amount of land has become affected by surface mineral working, and much of this devastation has been left in a derelict state. The yearly output of all the major minerals worked by surface excavations increased three to fourfold in the fifteen years 1922 to 1937, and again more than doubled in the fifteen years to 1952. Apart from the new industry of opencast coal extraction, sand and gravel production has shown the greatest increase, output rising twenty-five-fold in thirty years.

The current rate for all mineral requirements for direct extraction is nearly 6,000 acres per year with another 5,000 acres required for ancillary needs (Table 18). To this has also to be added a further 1,000 acres for the disposal of mineral wastes, urban and industrial refuse, and an unpredictable area which is made derelict by subsidence. As a result the annual gross rate of land loss is about 12,000 acres, of which over 5,500 acres are graded as first-class land (categories 1 to 4) by the Land Utilisation Survey of Great Britain. It is generally argued that this loss is wasteful of the Nation's agricultural resources and that the land should be restored wherever possible. Indeed, restoration is made compulsory on new ironstone and all opencast coal-workings. Local planning authorities also have the power to impose restoration conditions on all other types of workings and current policies ensure that about 60 per cent of the present devastations should be restored. Therefore, the final annual net loss is only about 3,500 acres.

In our research at Wye College we have attempted to analyse the results of these policies to determine whether or not the restoration of these 8,500 acres each year is an economic proposition in its own right. In the main, the approach has been by a selection of case-studies of individual restorations. In all types of workings restored the vital factor determining profitability has been found to be that of treatment costs. Almost always these vary more than the returns no matter what after-use has occurred. These costs cannot, however, be discussed in isolation without reference both to the types of working being restored and the different after-uses.

We shall deal with the after-uses first. The majority of current restorations are being made to agriculture—most of the ironstone and coal by law and over half the sand and gravel workings. In all but a negligible number of sand and gravel pits, studies of their restoration problems have shown the costs to be very high indeed because of the levelling and after-treatment required. Forestry involves almost equally expensive restoration if high cost levelling operations are required. But this type of levelling is by no means necessary for afforestation, and before State grants were given for both levelling and tree-planting, several profitable plantations were created on unlevelled land in the Midlands. Experience from the United States suggests that trees often thrive better on unlevelled spoil. If the major cost of levelling were dispensed with, afforestation of devastated surface mineral workings could be undertaken very cheaply indeed, especially in rabbit-free areas. Urban and industrial after-uses are only possible on a few favourably located workings. In these cases costs are generally less than for agriculture because, although levelling may have to be undertaken,

Table 18

THE SURFACE WORKING OF MINERALS IN ENGLAND AND WALES.
ESTIMATE OF ANNUAL LAND DEVASTATION

Use	Direct working	Ancillary needs	Total Gross Loss	Proportion probably restorable	Total Net Loss
	acs.	acs.	acs.	%	acs.
Opencast Coal......	2200	4500	6700	95	335
Sand and Gravel....	1750	250	2000	50	1000
Ironstone	550	50	600	95	30
Clay	400	40	440	15	374
Limestone..........	250	20	270	—	270
Chalk	200	20	220	—	220
Silica sand	140	10	150	10	135
Igneous rock	100	10	110	—	110
Ball and china clay..	40	20	60	—	60
Sandstone..........	30	—	30	—	30
Other, say..........	100	—	100	—	100
Colliery and other mineral wastes....	750	—	750	—	750
Industrial, urban and domestic refuse ..	500	—	500	75	125
Subsidence	?	—	?	—	?
Total.............	7010	4920	11930		3539
'say'	7000		12000		3500

after-treatments are generally few. Subsequent development
values are higher on sites near towns, and profits often result
therefrom.

Most of the after-uses retaining flooded pits in a wet use
are low-cost and therefore profitable, and it is difficult to
make out an economic case for the filling of any pits, wet
or dry, unless they are naturally in demand for the disposal
of wastes. The cost of transporting 'fill' is high, and whether
the filling of a pit is a liability or an asset to the community
depends almost entirely upon its position in relation to alternative disposal points and the sources of available filling
material.

The findings of our studies can only be put in more concrete
terms by reference to the problems of different types of surface mineral workings. The most common and the most

expensive may well be considered first. This is the obligatory restoration of opencast coal and ironstone sites to agriculture. If no treatment were undertaken, these sites would be left derelict, in the main in 'hill and dale' formation with, in the case of coal sites at least, a final open cut next to the high wall. The current restoration code, however, requires that the sites be levelled and graded in with the surrounding land and recovered with saved topsoil. The costs for making this type of restoration ranged, in the early 1950's, from about £400 to over £2,200 per acre depending on actual site conditions. Subsequent to this, further treatment is necessary to make the land ready for full agricultural practices; costs for this averaged about £100 per acre for a five-year treatment. The resultant agricultural productivity was valued, however, at only about 60 per cent of the site's previous worth, or even less where compaction was caused by the levelling operations, or where liability to further settlement was severe.

If we take the lowest figure of the range of costs of restoration, i.e. £400 per acre and add to it a weighted average figure of the cost of agricultural pre-treatment, there is a minimal capital charge of £500 per acre. The agricultural productivity of most of the land earmarked for opencast coal or ironstone working is only at or below average so that our case studies showed the agricultural average output of the restored land, at 1955–6 values, to be £25 or below, this figure being net of purchases of seeds, animal and feeding stuffs from other farms. As this type of opencast mineral working is usually large-scale, involving entire farms rather than merely odd fringe fields, the fixed and variable costs of producing this output must be deducted to give the net return to this land on which £500 has been spent. This net return varies greatly according to the skill of individual farmers but at this time was unlikely to average more than £7 per acre. This return represents only 1·4 per cent on the capital used. It is obvious that with a range of full restoration costs of between £500 and £2,300, most of the sites showed a net return of well under 1 per cent.

In terms of food replacement, the capital costs of replacing the agricultural production of the land used for the opencast working of coal and ironstone appear to represent a range of £820 to £3,772 per urbanised acre. These figures can be contrasted with the comparable figure of £351 per urbanised acre involved in comprehensive schemes of improvement on hill and upland farms and of £118 to £225 on coastal reclamation for agricultural use. It is, therefore, from these comparisons, difficult to justify the complete agricultural restoration of opencast coal and ironstone sites on either economic or agricultural grounds, though there are many important amenity and social reasons in favour of doing some sort of restoration.

More economic is the agricultural restoration of dry sand and gravel pits which do not require filling. In this case costs are lower as less levelling has to be undertaken and topsoil is not always saved, either because of its virtual absence from many sites or because of the greater amenability to agricultural treatment of the post-working surface. Even where soil is saved and respread, costs are less than with the restoration of opencast coal and ironstone sites chiefly because of the possibility of employing different methods involving direct restoration or shorter transport distances. Any necessary agricultural after-treatments are fewer and cheaper, and the returns are higher because the sites possess a more favourable geological structure. On high-level gravel deposits the post-restoration value of the site may even be higher than the pre-working one as the restored surface is less liable to dry out in summer. Average costs for restorations ranged, in the early 1950's, from £30 to about £200 per acre, with a weighted average of approximately £100.

Very often, too, these reclaimed sand and gravel pits can be added to the acreage of a nearby farm and this makes their use in agriculture much more economic in the same way as the reclamation of odd pieces of derelict woodland. Net returns of £10 per acre from the agricultural use of such reclaimed pits are quite reasonable to expect when farmed in this way, and this is a reward on the extra capital of £100 of 10 per cent. The food replacement figure would be around £137 of capital per urbanised acre.

Where pits require filling before a dry use can be made of them the profitability of the enterprise depends almost entirely upon the proximity of the pit to the sources of 'fill' being used. In areas where places for refuse disposal are scarce, pit owners can make charges upon the refuse disposers and by so doing can sometimes even cover their other costs of restoration and finally sell the finished site at a profit. But this does not really show the true cost of the work, for the real costs are but transferred to other sections of the community. The actual costs of tipping in that particular pit can only be determined by comparing the cost of tipping there with the costs of tipping on alternative sites or of disposing of the refuse in other ways. Because the transport of refuse costs up to 6d. per ton/mile for every acre/foot tipped the saving of one mile distance is worth about £40. Thus the saving on an 'average' pit of 15 feet in depth would be about £600 per acre. Conversely, if 'fill' has to be diverted to a pit from a disposal point nearer to the source of supply, then the extra cost of transport must be regarded as a charge on the restoration. Alternative methods of disposing of the 'fill' used have also to be considered. These may include mechanical means, in moderation, though these methods are more expensive than controlled tipping. Therefore, apart from any transport differences involved, the controlled filling of a derelict pit may also lead to a community saving of about £150 per acre/foot (or over £2,000 for a 15-foot pit) if no other tipping sites at all are available.

The same considerations also apply to other derelict sites requiring filling, though the restoration of subsidence hollows, because of their general location in more widely derelict areas, also requires consideration in the context of larger district or regional schemes (for example, as at Walsall and Wigan). With such schemes it may often be possible to make a net capital gain.

Where dry pits needing filling are remote from sources of 'fill' little can be done, and they must be left derelict unless such uses as military training grounds, nature reserves or rough-shooting are possible. If flooded, however, a wet use can often be made of them. Depending on their size the possible uses are as fishing reserves, lidos, yachting lakes, aquadromes and water reservoirs. Their profitability may depend more on local demand than on cost, though treatments are not often expensive.

The final areas of dereliction to consider are those of large spoil mounds which are mostly of colliery waste. Some have been restored by levelling and regrading under the Distribution of Industry Act, but our analyses have shown them to be extremely expensive with costs ranging from about £600 to as much as £12,000 per acre, the weighted average of eighteen cases being over £2,000 per acre. In no case could any after-use in these areas repay more than a small fraction of the costs involved. Some of the tips have been afforested, and this seems often to be the least uneconomic use and it has some extra value from the point of view of amenity.

In general, it can be said that the types of restorations which are most likely to be profitable are those of afforestation and, possibly, the restoration of flooded pits to wet uses, because both require few treatments and are thus low in cost. Conversely, restorations for agricultural uses are largely unprofitable because of their high cost and low returns, except in the restoration of odd dry sand and gravel pits for adding to existing farms. Lastly, the profitability of urban, industrial or other restorations, including those where filling is required, varies within wide limits, and can really only be determined by detailed study of each individual restoration proposed.

Some comparisons

What conclusions, then, can we tentatively make about the winning of new land in the lowlands? The reclamation of odd pieces which can be incorporated into the adjoining farms

---

When the provision of single houses at low cost is considered all important, large areas of land and difficult problems of providing attractive layouts are involved. All countries, and not only Great Britain and the United States, are meeting such problems because of the world-wide emphasis on the creation of detached dwellings. Long Island, New York.

Aerofilm

without involving them in major increases in their fixed costs is obviously worth while, both to the individual farmer and to the nation. These odd pieces can be reclaimed from derelict woodland, dry sand and gravel workings and small accretions of land along our coasts. Even small areas of common land which have lost their social usefulness could probably be integrated into the economy of nearby farms with profit.

The nation could usefully show more interest in, and give more practical and financial help to, the winning of suitable land from the sea, even when this involves the heavier costs of creating new farms. It also should try to record more completely the results actually being obtained from expenditure on various forms of land drainage. This is important as good drainage is an expensive operation and we need to know more clearly what return we are getting back from present expenditure and what we could expect from an acceleration of the drainage programme. Remembering that many foreigners say 'England would be a lovely country if it had a roof,' we should be more keenly aware of the problem and of the economics of getting rid of the surplus water which comes down so copiously at times.

The complete restoration of opencast coal and ironstone workings to agriculture appears to be a very expensive proposition in the comparative studies we have been able to make. This does not necessarily suggest an abandonment of all restoration for agriculture but it does point to the need for more critical examination of each site so as to use cheap methods of reclamation and to more flexibility in the after-use. In particular, the nation might well gain if there is a greater degree of afforestation of such sites and if, on some occasions, the original farms were not reconstructed but the reclaimed land added to surrounding farms.

It is now time to move on from the consideration of possible areas of new land in the hills and the lowlands in order to try to answer the question 'But surely it would be better to

---

The grimness of living in the older and more thickly populated parts of the great cities is partially alleviated by some carefully preserved open spaces. Paddington, London.

Aerofilm

G

intensify the use of the land we still have in agricultural use rather than to attempt to bring in new land?' The next section deals with some of the problems and methods of intensifying farming systems.

The intensification of agricultural production

In a commercial agriculture, the degree of intensity of land use within it is a relative matter. Certainly, an overall price level for agricultural produce that is high in relation to the prices of other things in the national economy enables farmers to get high incomes from small areas of land. But if the farming fabric is made up of large farms, this intensification may be inhibited by high overall agricultural prices because satisfactory personal incomes can be obtained from farming at a lower level than formerly. The intensity of use of a piece of farming land does depend so much on the size of the whole farm of which it forms part.

When a holding is small, the land is usually put to an intensive use because of the need to earn an income large enough to support the farmer and his family. Because many costs in farming are of a fixed or overhead nature, a large output is necessary to obtain a return more than adequate to cover all of them. This is why small farms tend to concentrate on the production of crops like vegetables and fruit, and livestock products such as pigs, poultry and milk. All of these can give a relatively high output per acre of land, especially if use is made of animal feeding stuffs purchased from larger farms elsewhere, either at home or abroad. This emphasis on size of output on small farms is very important because studies of farming profitability in recent years[1] have shown that the bulk of small farms which fail to attain satisfactory incomes for their occupiers fail because their total output is inadequate.

On the other hand, there are more practical alternatives to the use of a piece of land belonging to a large farm. The farmer can use it to grow crops giving a high output per

---

[1] For example, Reid, I. G., *The Small Farm on Heavy Land*, Wye College, University of London, June 1958, and Sturrock, F. G., and Wallace, D. N., *The Family Farm*, University of Cambridge, 1957.

acre such as sugar beet, potatoes, field vegetables like peas or cabbage, or intensive grazing of leys with silage making. But this will involve him in much work and heavy costs. As an alternative he may consider other systems of land use which give him lower total returns per acre but very much less work, worry and costs. Such systems of using land more extensively are the grazing of cattle and sheep and the growing of cereals.

In a family farm type of agriculture there is, then, a progressive decline in the intensity of land use as size of farm increases. It will be noticed from Table 19 that both output and expenditure per acre decline as size of farm increased. There is not very much change in the profit per acre in the figures shown but obviously a great change in the profitability of the whole farm. At a profit level of £7 an acre, a 50-acre farm nets a profit of £350, a 300-acre farm more than £2,000 a year.

Much of the production on the smaller farms comes from the use of products grown on other land, at home and abroad. The buying of animal feeding stuffs is really a way of

Table 19

THE DECLINE IN INTENSITY OF FARMING AS SIZE OF HOLDING
INCREASES

Financial Results of 167 farms in South-East England 1955–56, in £'s per acre

	Output	All Expenses	Purchased Feed	Profit (or Management and investment income)
50 acres and under........	91	84	31	7
51 to 100 acres	57	51	17	6
101 to 150 acres..........	46	40	11	6
151 to 300 acres..........	43	38	9	5
Over 300 acres	39	32	6	7
All Farms	51	45	13	6

adding to the farm acreage. As farms become larger the buying in of such animal feeding stuffs becomes less and less important in relative terms. The difference in farm size alone is, therefore, responsible for quite substantial changes in the intensity with which individual fields may be used. Although lying side by side, they may belong to different occupiers with different size holdings.

Within the individual farm, the decision as to which crops to grow and which form of livestock to keep greatly affects the intensity of land use. A glance at the 'standard' outputs obtained from different crops and livestock, as given in Table 20, shows a great range in intensity. These are, of course, average results drawn from the experience of many farms differing in soil, shape and size and from farmers of differing ability. The outputs can be greatly increased by raising yields, and the need for high yields is greater on the farms with small acreages because of their need for a high turnover. This need is not always realised in practice as often small farms are on poor land. It is on the larger farms that modern technical knowledge, allied with capital equipment, has been most successfully applied to the growing of good crops and livestock.

Some other decisions of the individual farmer are also of major importance in deciding the general level of his farming intensity. One is the proportion of his land used for arable cropping as compared with that used for the rearing or feeding of livestock. Another is the proportion of the arable land that is used for growing crops which are sold directly off the farm as against the non-cash crops which are further processed by feeding through livestock. If the efficiency of conversion through the livestock is low it is easy to lower the intensity of the whole farming system by growing too many arable crops for livestock feeding.

This question of 'feed economy'—the efficiency, in financial terms, of the growing or buying in of feeding stuffs for animals and their conversion into animal products—is vital to most British mixed farms, as, in so many cases, it is in this section of the farm's activities that inefficiency so quickly occurs and can remain hidden. It is so easy for crops such as grass used for grazing, hay and silage, or forage crops like kale and home-grown oats and barley to be badly used in the

Table 20

STANDARD OUTPUTS* OF SOME DIFFERENT AGRICULTURAL
ENTERPRISES ARRANGED IN ORDER OF MAGNITUDE

	Standard output £s per acre
Top Fruit—dessert	250
culinary	150
Soft Fruit (excluding strawberries)	180
Potatoes	100
Sugar Beet	70
Peas for canning	50
Wheat	35
Barley	33
Oats	25
	£ per animal kept
Dairy cows	110
Sow	80
Cattle over 2 years old	30
Beef cow	25
Breeding ewes	10
Poultry over 6 months old	3

* The Standard output is the annual money value, per acre or per animal, of the production expected according to average yields and at 1957–8 prices.

feeding of livestock so that the farm's output in terms of saleable goods is low even though the farm's physical productivity may appear high.

If a farmer sets out to be really efficient in making high and continuous profits in farming he is involved immediately in two sets of problems. In the first place, the basic plan or policy of the farm must be sound. This means that the balance between livestock and crops for sale or for feeding must match up to the farmer's own personal interests and ability, to the relative price levels for these different products and to the resources of labour, capital and land which are available or could be made available. If the plan is ill conceived, no amount of good husbandry will give a really satisfactory result.

Given the satisfactory plan or policy, a farmer's second set of problems is to be efficient in each aspect of the practical operation of this plan. The cows chosen must be regular breeders and good converters of food into milk, sows kept must regularly raise large litters of pigs which reach market weight with least food and trouble. The crops it has been decided worth while to grow must give the yields necessary for the success of the plan.

Thus, this problem of intensive or extensive systems of farming involves thousands of individual farms of various sizes with different quantities of available capital. These farmers have different plans—some good, some adequate, some bad. These farm policies are either carried out well, adequately or badly. Is it any wonder then that all kinds of degrees of intensity in food production are found scattered throughout agricultural Britain?

The costs and returns from intensifying British agriculture

These need to be looked at not only in relation to combating the losses of agricultural output caused by urbanisation but also as a possible means of raising efficiency, reducing unit costs of production and, if desired, reducing the amount of State help to agriculture.

A recent study of this general problem is pertinent to the argument.[1] The authors, Cheveley and Price, suggest that increasing output is the best way to raise the economic efficiency of most British farms because of the importance of fixed costs in commercial agricultural production. To do this they believe that there must be increased production of cattle and sheep, through improved grassland and the erection of labour-saving buildings. This type of programme obviously involves additional capital, and Cheveley and Price suggested that an average investment of £2,000 (at 1954 prices) is needed on each farm in the United Kingdom. Budgets were prepared to use £230,000,000 of new capital on improved farm buildings and other fixed equipment. Another £100,000,000 would be involved in a programme of land reclamation and improvement and £109,000,000 on the extra sheep and cattle needed to use the improved grassland.

[1] Cheveley, S., and Price, O., *Capital in United Kingdom Agriculture— Present and Future*, Imperial Chemical Industries Ltd., 1955.

The implementation of this budget was planned to cover a five-year period. During these years there would, naturally, be an increase in farm working costs (fertilisers, lime, grass seeds, fencing, drainage, maintenance and depreciation) on the more intensive systems of farming though these would be compensated in part by savings in purchases of feeding stuffs.

The conclusions of this analysis were that there should be, by the sixth year of the budget, an increased annual output of agricultural products valued at £108,600,000 on a new capital investment of £439,000,000. The additional costs of this, minus a saving in purchases of feeding stuffs, would be £48,200,000, leaving an additional net income of £60,400,000 to the farmer. This would be a return on capital of 13·8 per cent.

There has been some discussion about these proposals of Cheveley and Price, but for the purposes of our study of the possibilities of 'new' land in the lowlands they represent a serious attempt to make a cost-benefit analysis of a general programme of agricultural intensification, mainly through the improved use of grass, marketed through extra sheep and beef cattle. The estimate can be cast in the form of the Food Replacement concept so that it can be compared with some of the other forms of new and improved agricultural land use previously examined in this and in earlier chapters.

In 1955–6 the average 'net' agricultural output of agricultural crops and grass was £25 per acre.

The increase in 'net' output, postulated by Cheveley and Price, was £108,600,000 on 31,130,000 acres in the United Kingdom

that is, £3·5 per acre

The extra capital suggested as needed to secure this increase in 'net' output is £439,000,000 throughout the United Kingdom

that is, £14·07 per acre

The 'net' agricultural output, in 1955–6, of the land earmarked for planned urban development was £41 per acre.

Therefore the capital necessary to replace this output through general intensification of the remaining agricultural land is $\dfrac{14\cdot07}{3\cdot5} \times 41$

$$\text{that is} = \underline{£165}$$

This amount of capital would be spread over $\dfrac{41}{3\cdot5}$ or $11\cdot7$ acres.

These calculations suggest that, if the Cheveley and Price budgets were achieved in practice, the net agricultural output of each acre of the land zoned for new urban development in Great Britain could be replaced by the investment of £165 in the intensification of agriculture on each $11\frac{1}{2}$ acres of the farm land that remains.

We have looked at a range of possibilities in the gaining of 'new' land in the hills and uplands and in the lowlands, together with some discussion of the problem of intensification of agricultural production on the land already in agricultural use. By using the concept of food replacement, it is possible to relate these schemes for land reclamation, land restoration and land intensification to each other and to look at the likely costs and returns involved in the light of the progressive urbanisation of the agricultural land of this country. In the next chapter the argument is applied to the problem of trying to measure the agricultural significance of a large area of valuable farm land which has recently been considered as a site for a new town.

THE competition between urban growth and agriculture is seen in its most dramatic form in proposals to build large towns in areas where there is no major community already established. There have been a number of such cases since 1945 in Great Britain because of the Labour Government's policy of encouraging the creation of a number of new towns and the Conservative Government's policy of completing them.

Under the New Towns Act of 1946, areas for new towns could be designated by the Government after the holding of a public inquiry. All work such as housing, roads and factories needed for the town's development was placed under the control of a Development Corporation for that particular area which is independent of local authorities but dependent on Government financing for its economic support. Of the eight new towns designated in the London region between 1946 and 1949 all, by 1956, had moved more than one-third of the way towards the targets set—which were usually to a population of about 60,000 persons each. Some of these towns, such as Bracknell, Harlow and Stevenage, were expansions of settlements previously little more than villages in size. Others such as Welwyn, Hatfield, Basildon, Hemel Hempstead and Crawley were already partly urbanised. Several other new towns have been established in other parts of Great Britain since the end of World War II such as Corby in Northamptonshire, Cwmbran in Monmouthshire, Newton Aycliffe and Peterlee in County Durham, and Glenrothes, Cumbernauld and East Kilbride in Scotland.

In the discussions as to the siting of these new towns physical agricultural considerations were taken into account and some of the sites proposed in the Greater London Plan, such as Meopham in Kent and White Waltham in Berkshire, were turned down on agricultural grounds. But no systematic comparison of the present or potential productivity of the agricultural land involved was made in relation to differences in development costs on alternative new town sites.

Recently an opportunity arose to measure the productivity of a large area of farm land being considered as a site for a new town to cater for the housing overspill of Manchester. For more than ten years this particular city has been attempting to secure a large site outside its boundaries on which to build a sizeable town. Because of the growth of industry in the Trafford Park area, the city council has tried to choose a site within daily travelling distance of this area. The most attractive and cheapest sites to develop close to Manchester have been to the south of the city, in the neighbouring county of Cheshire. There is a long history of argument and delays in relation to such a new town site and the latest action by the Government has been the second rejection of Manchester's case to develop a new town at Lymm, following a public inquiry held in January 1958 by an inspector independent of any Government department.

At this last public inquiry attempts were made to measure the value of the agricultural productivity of the 3,000 odd acres of north Cheshire which were under consideration at Lymm. The evidence was only directly relevant if it could be proved that Manchester needed an area large enough for a new town *in addition to* sites available to her for housing within her own boundary and within the boundaries of nearby towns. As it so happened, the independent inspector reported that he did not find Manchester's case for such a new town area proved and the Government turned down the Lymm proposal on these grounds. The final decision was influenced only to a small extent by the evidence given as to the local and national importance of the farm land at Lymm.[1]

The Lymm site provided, however, an important case study in which concepts and measures discussed in this book could be applied in order to measure the value to the nation of a very fertile stretch of agricultural land.

[1] Ministry of Housing and Local Government, 'Report of Inquiry into the Proposed Development of Land at Lymm for Manchester Overspill,' H.M.S.O., 1958.

For the first inquiry in 1953 and again for that in 1958 the Cheshire branch of the National Farmers' Union made surveys of the land and farms affected by the Manchester proposal to develop the area around the small village of Lymm. With the information provided by these 'production surveys,' as they were called, supplemented by vital extra information and estimates, an attempt was made to measure the contribution to national wealth resulting from man's use of this well-farmed stretch of English countryside.

The first step in such an evaluation is to record the physical quantities and financial value of the crops and livestock products sold off the land over a number of recent financial years. The gross production has to be adjusted for changes in the valuations of farm livestock and produce on hand at the beginning and end of each farming year. This is important in order to arrive at the true output of each farm during a year's operation. The financial value of the crops and livestock sold is necessary for this evaluation as otherwise, with only physical descriptions and quantities, the planning inspector who has the task of comparing the agricultural case with other town and country planning considerations, will be confronted only with masses of physical data like gallons of milk produced, numbers of animals of different type, age and weight sold and dozens of lettuces marketed.

On the 3,075 acres of agricultural land affected at Lymm, details of the numbers of animals and weights of crops sold were available for the calendar years of 1952 and 1957, and prices were allocated to these at the levels prevailing at these times. Details of the actual prices received by the farmers concerned would have been better but they had not been collected in the 'production surveys.'

The second task is to record the expenses involved in obtaining this production; such as the costs incurred on hired labour, livestock purchases, bought in feeding stuffs, tractor fuel, machinery and repairs and so forth. All production, whether of farm products or of anything else, involves using other resources like hired labour, raw materials, bought equipment and fuel. If these resources had not been used on the Lymm farms they could have been used, at least in part, on other farms or in other lines of production. The cost of their use should therefore be recorded and taken away from the gross production of the land in order to find the net contribution resulting from the use of this area for agricultural purposes.

As details of costs from the particular farms were not available at either inquiry, allowances were made for such farm expenses on the basis of the level of these items experienced on comparable types of farms in north Cheshire, as given in the reports on 'Farm Incomes' published annually by the Ministry of Agriculture, Fisheries and Food. Amongst these items of cost, it is important to have information on the products bought in from other farms, such as purchased feeding stuffs, seed and livestock. This is necessary in order to record the production, its character and amount, actually created by the land of Lymm, with all the processing of food on that land eliminated. It is common practice on many farms to buy feeding stuffs produced on other farms and to turn these into milk or meat. In a similar way, store and breeding animals from other farms are often brought in and processed by fattening. These 'imports' from other areas and farms must be deducted from the gross production of any land in order to get a true picture of what is produced by that land. Without this sort of correction, poor land can be made to appear very productive by reason of its use to process other farm products, and good land, not used for a processing type of food production, made to look relatively insignificant in its contribution to food supplies.

Records, or failing these, estimates, are also necessary of the value of the farm produce consumed by the farm family and the amount of unpaid family labour involved in farm work. Without recording such items, errors of some magnitude can occur in the totals of both farm revenue and farm costs.

The value added by the agricultural use of the Lymm site

A number of calculations were necessary for each farm and piece of land in order to show the real contribution made in agricultural use. All of these were of a simple nature.

The gross annual production is the first important figure. This is the total of sales of livestock and crop products, adjusted for differences between opening and closing valuations plus allowances for produce consumed by the farm family or given to farm staff as perquisites. Such calculations for the 3,075 acres of land under discussion for urban development at Lymm showed that the area had, in the 1950's, a gross agricultural production of £81·1 per acre per year—or a total for the area of about £249,000 annually. This figure is considerably above the £53 per acre which was calculated to be the average gross output, in 1955–6, of all the farming land zoned for urban development in the Development Plans submitted for approval. There is no doubt, therefore, that the agricultural contribution of the farmed land at Lymm is very good and its output of milk, combined with cash arable crops, is comparable with famous specialised and intensive cropping areas such as the Ormskirk region of Lancashire. It is lower, however, than the average of market garden and cash crop holdings in England and Wales (£115 per acre).

It might be argued that the contribution to national wealth of retaining the Lymm area in agricultural use is roughly £250,000 a year. Yet this is a gross contribution only and to get the value added by this particular area we must deduct the total expenses involved in farming this land. These were estimated to be, on average, £71·6 per acre and this figure, deducted from the £81·1 of gross output, leaves a margin of £9·5. This £9·5 is the net farm income, or the sum available, per acre, to reward the occupiers for their own efforts and the use of their own capital in the business of farming. On the 3,075 acres affected it represents an annual value of £29,212.

These estimates, of £249,000 of gross production and of £29,212 of net farm income, are based on the fortunes of farming in the year 1952–3. The collection of factual data by the National Farmers' Union on the same area in 1957 made it possible to see if there had been any major change in the agricultural contribution of the Lymm area during the five years 1952 to 1957. The presence of the more up-to-date survey of 1957 was valuable but, as it had been carried out on exactly the same lines as the earlier survey, the same adjustments and assumptions had to be made in order to get the facts into a usable and comparative form. It would have been much better for the purposes of these two Inquiries if a survey on the lines of the Farm Management Survey of the University Departments of Agricultural Economics had been made.

A careful review of the 1957 data for the area and of changes in farming costs and returns in the intervening years led us to the conclusion that the figure of £29,212 as the net annual agricultural contribution of the Lymm land and farmers was fair in relation to the five-year period. The main reasons for this conclusion were:

(1) A comparative study of the two production surveys showed that the value of the *increased* sales of agricultural produce from the Lymm farms in 1957, as compared with 1952, came to £30,464. The particular commodities showing increased sales, in descending order of importance, were wheat, fat pigs, milk, barley, oats, store cattle, hay, fat sheep, mixed corn and calves. The value of *decreases* in sales in 1957 as against 1952 equalled £29,908, and these involved, again in descending order of importance, eggs, beef cattle, potatoes, store pigs, straw and roots. Thus the reduction in sales of certain products off the Lymm farms between these two years was counterbalanced by the increased sales of certain other farm products.

(2) The total financial value of the gross agricultural output of the Lymm site in 1957 was higher than in 1952, as the prices of beef and store cattle, sheep and lambs, barley and oats were higher and those of milk, eggs, potatoes, wheat, pigs, and poultry the same or only slightly lower. Yet the costs of production of these commodities increased to a similar extent between 1952 and 1957, leaving a net farm income of approximately the same amount in each of these years. The aggregate farming net income of the United Kingdom, adjusted for normal weather conditions, was, in 1952–3, £334,500,000 and was forecast for 1956–7 at £334,000,000. In all the intervening years between these two,

the net income of the 'national' farm was lower than £334,000,000.

(3) It is impossible to judge whether the efficiency of production on the Lymm farms between 1952 and 1957 had increased to the same extent as in the whole of national agriculture or by a greater or lesser amount. The local production surveys of 1952–3 and 1956–7 give little evidence on this point, except to show that the increase in output of milk per cow on the Lymm farms between 1952 and 1957 was about the same as the national increase between these two years.

It is felt, therefore, that the figure of £9·5 per farmed acre was a fair indication of the value of the agricultural income of the Lymm site over a fair period of time. Further deductions should now be made from this figure of £9·5 in order to give a more exact measure of the value added each year to the nation's wealth through the farming use of this land. We need to obtain the value of the contribution made by the land itself and this should exclude the value of the manual work and managerial skill of the farmer and his wife and also the reward owing to the farmer's own working capital. In theory, if the occupiers of the farms at Lymm were dispossessed in order to build a new town, these people would be able to use their manual and managerial skills on other farms or in other jobs and be paid for them at competitive rates. In addition, the working capital now involved would become freely available for investment elsewhere. In practice, the real values of alternative uses of a farmer's time and capital are debatable and it is difficult to measure or estimate the values involved. The type of analysis can be shown, however, by using rough estimates of these extra deductions (Table 21). In this way a figure of £4·9 per acre is obtained for the value added by the land alone.

The rate of discount to be used in capitalisation

The purpose of making these calculations of the value added each year by agricultural use of the Lymm area is in order to contrast them with the additional costs of site development which could be justified in the national interest

Table 21

*Calculation of the Value Added by the Existing Agricultural
Use of the Land* (1955–6)

		£ per acre
Gross agricultural revenue		81·1
All farm expenditure.........................		71·6
Net farm income, weighted by type of farm......		9·5
To obtain the value added by use of land alone:		
Add rent,* already deducted in total expenditure	+1·8	
Deduct interest* at 5 per cent on working capital of the farm, i.e. on £28·44 per acre	−1·4	
Deduct value of unpaid labour of farmer and wife†	−2·6	
Deduct for value of farmer's managerial ability (£560 for average 229-acre farms which are mixed with substantial dairying)..	−2·4	−4·6
Value added by the land alone...............		4·9

* Values of these items as given for the farming group 'Mixed with Substantial dairying' in *Farm Incomes*, 1955–6. Ministry of Agriculture, Fisheries and Food, Report No. 9.

† Value as given for the group 'Cheshire and North Shropshire—Dairying' in the above report.

in order to keep urban development off the Lymm area. As these additional costs are usually 'once and for all' costs incurred in the early stages of building operations, the problem of time preference comes in and, consequently, so does the rate of discount to be used in capitalising in perpetuity the annual increments of the agricultural contribution. Should the rate of discount used be a market rate which the individual would use in looking at the transaction from the point of view of his own private gain or some other social rate, rather lower than the level of market rates, arising because society can take a longer term view of such investments than can individuals?

The market rate of discount, even in agriculture, is short-term in operation. For example, in the years 1955 to 1957, as judged by the relationships between net farm incomes and the sale value of farms, the appropriate market rate of discount would be 7 per cent.[1] This represents a period of just over fourteen years' purchase. At this rate of 7 per cent, the capitalised value of the £9·5 net contribution from the Lymm farms totals £136 per acre, or £418,200 for the agricultural land of the whole site. If the value of the contribution made by the land alone is taken, that is, the estimate of £4·9 per acre, the appropriate market rate of discount to use in capitalising this theoretical rental value is 4 per cent or twenty-five years' purchase.[2] This gives a capital value of £122 per acre, in contrast with the figure of £136 derived from the earlier calculation.

On the other hand, it can be argued that a social rate of discount should be taken rather than the market rate at a particular point in time. The market rate is influenced by short-term factors and by the short-term outlook of most private individuals. In making a long-term and probably permanent change in land use, surely the State should take a longer term view and accept a lower rate of discount as satisfactory? Market rates are geared to the normal life expectation of individuals, and no individual places much value on benefits accruing after his death. But society, on the other hand, is immortal and thus has to put a much higher value on distant benefits.

The experience gained and actions taken by the Dutch in their reclamation of land from the former Zuider Zee are pertinent here. A number of 'polders' have been reclaimed and equipped for farming purposes in the past half century. In all cases the cost of the work has been well above the value placed on the new land for agricultural use when it has arrived at a condition fit to be used. Although the total costs of reclamation and the agricultural and rental

[1] Ward, J. T., 'The Siting of Urban Development in Agricultural Land,' *The Journal of Agricultural Economics*, Vol. XII, No. 4, December 1957, p. 458.

[2] Ward, J. T., *Farm Rents and Tenure*, Estates Gazette Ltd., London, 1959.

values placed on the new land have varied greatly through the years, the general trend being upwards, the costs of reclamation of each area of land have been approximately twice as high as the value for commercial farming finally placed on it by the valuation experts when the particular area of land was judged to be ready for commercial use.

This Dutch experience is particularly appropriate to the problem of competition between agricultural and urban uses of land when it is realised that the amount of new land brought into agricultural use by polder-reclamation has only balanced the area of Holland being taken out of agricultural use by the growth of their towns and cities. It means that the Dutch democracy, through its elected representatives, have acted as though the social rate of discount to be used in agricultural-urban comparisons of land use is not the market rate of discount but a rate approximately half as great.

Can we obtain any guidance on this matter from British experience and action on investment in major improvements to agricultural land? The discussion in Chapter 8 on the capital costs and returns of agricultural rehabilitation in the hills and uplands of Great Britain is pertinent. It will be seen that our society—again democratic as in Holland and through the action of its elected Parliament—has of late years been investing national capital in hill farm improvements giving returns well below market rates of interest. Evidence given in that chapter suggests that these returns have not been running at above 4 to 5 per cent if the large investments in social improvements (that is, in the renovation of farm-houses, road improvements and provision of better services of piped water, grid electricity and local schools) are taken into account.

Another comparison can be made using the yardstick of food replacement. It has already been suggested that the various possibilities of land reclamation and land upgrading can be usefully compared by relating the cost and returns from such improvement to the level of output of food produced on the land which will be lost to urban growth. Thus, as shown in Chapter 4, the average value in 1955–6 of the 'net' agricultural output of all the land zoned for development in the 1950–70 town plans was £41 per acre. At that value, the highest cost of major land improvement (that on hill and upland farms discussed in Chapter 8) represented £351 of new capital. If the output from the Lymm land, net of 'imports' of seeds, feeding stuffs and animals from other farms, is of the same order as the national figures of £53 gross representing £41 'net,' then the gross Lymm production of £81 per acre is of the order of £63, 'net' of these 'imports.' To replace this level of production on a sustained basis from improvements to hill and upland farms would involve about

£351 $\times \dfrac{63}{41}$ or £540 for each agricultural acre lost at Lymm.

Obviously, there would be a number of cheaper ways than this of replacing the food output of the Lymm farms—by more intensive use of better-quality lower land, reclamation of unused land or derelict woodland in certain areas and, possibly, through payment for increased food imports. But this figure of £540 for each agricultural acre of Lymm does represent a maximum replacement cost within the agricultural sector of the British economy.

In the discussion of the possibilities of obtaining new land in the lowlands of this country, it is shown that certain major proposals made recently by Cheveley and Price for the intensification of existing agricultural land use suggest a food replacement capital cost of £165 per urbanised acre. In relation to the higher than average quality land at Lymm, this replacement figure rises to £254. Therefore the replacement of the existing output from Lymm farms by intensifying production on remaining farms would cost in extra capital about double the market value (£122 to £136) of the Lymm land in its present agricultural use.

This discussion of the Dutch experience and the food replacement calculations suggests that the use of social rates of discount at a level of one-half of the respective market rates is reasonable in the evaluation of a permanent change in use of a large stretch of agricultural land. It means, for example, the use of a rate of $3\frac{1}{2}$ per cent, rather than 7, to obtain the capitalised value in perpetuity of the £9·5 per acre of net farm income from the Lymm farms. At this rate the capitalised value per acre is £272 or, for the whole site of 3,075 acres, a sum of £834,643. Again, the estimated figure of £4·9 per acre, which represents the value added by the land alone, gives capitalised values of £245 per acre or £753,375 for the whole site if a rate of 2 rather than 4 per cent is used to capitalise this estimated rental value figure. Another method of arriving at a capitalised value is to use the food replacement capital cost for, say, the intensification of the remaining agricultural land in the country. This particular figure has been calculated as £254 of new capital to replace the 'net' output of each acre of Lymm farm land. This represents £781,050 over the whole of the new town site.

What is the significance of these calculations? They suggest that the *extra* capital cost that can be justified by redeveloping land already in urban use or by using a site of practically no agricultural value, such as heath or scrub land, is of the order of £750,000 to £840,000. It will be worth this extra expense to society in general in order to avoid the loss of the agricultural output of the 3,075 acres of Lymm farmland. Thus, for example, if Manchester accommodated the persons planned for Lymm within the existing urban areas by increasing the density of development, then this could be a right decision (but only in relation to the urban-agricultural part of the complete town planning case) if the extra costs imposed by the tightening up of densities came to under £840,000. If the costs were well above this figure then, other things being equal, it would be better for the agricultural land at Lymm to be taken rather than to increase the residential density of land already in urban uses.

If there are alternative major sites of differing agricultural qualities, then we can get some idea of the additional capital costs which can be justified if poorer areas of farm land are chosen in place of the Lymm site. Alternative sites of definite location and area were difficult to isolate from the proceedings of the 1958 Lymm Inquiry but, in the earlier Inquiry, the area around the village of Mobberley, to the south of Manchester, had been strongly considered as a possible new town site. Although turned down following the 1953 Inquiry on a number of grounds, the main one being the likelihood of subsidence problems from salt mining, there was also a strong agricultural objection to it. But was this agricultural objection really of greater, lesser or the same degree as that raised against the use of Lymm? And what would be the size of this difference in relation to differences in the ease and cost of developing Mobberley as a new town instead of Lymm? These questions were not asked during the 1953 Inquiry and even if they had been the factual information was not available in the evidence presented to answer them.

In the 1953 Inquiry, a 'production survey' was made for the Mobberley area by the Cheshire branch of the National Farmers' Union of exactly similar character to the surveys of agricultural use and production produced for the Lymm site in 1952 and 1957. If similar assumptions and adjustments are made to the Mobberley production survey as have already been made to those for Lymm, the agricultural significance of Mobberley as against Lymm can be evaluated.

Table 22

A COMPARISON OF THE AGRICULTURAL CONTRIBUTION OF LYMM
AND MOBBERLEY NEW TOWN SITES

	Lymm	*Mobberley*
Area (land in agricultural use)......	3,075 acres	3,009½ acres
	per acre	*per acre*
	£	£
Annual gross agricultural output ..	81·1	57·8
Annual farm expenditure..........	71·6	51·1
Net farm income per year..........	9·5	6·7
Net farm income capitalised in perpetuity at 3½ per cent		
per acre	272	191
for the whole site	834,643	576,104
Difference in favour of the Lymm site	£258,539	

The comparative figures given in Table 22 suggest that the difference in agricultural quality between the Lymm and Mobberley areas is sufficient to justify the expenditure of about an extra £250,000 on site works at Mobberley in order to avoid disturbing the present agricultural use of Lymm.

The weaknesses of these techniques

Any person who propounds a different way of measuring things from the method in actual practice must ask himself if there are serious weaknesses in his 'better way.' There are, of course, always strong forces in favour of carrying on as before in most situations even if these ways involve a lot of work and yet give an incomplete appreciation. This may be true in relation to the existing mode of presentation of the agricultural aspects of town and country planning. But more often the reason for non-use of a different concept or technique is that its disadvantages or weaknesses outweigh any good points that it might have. There are certainly weaknesses in the concepts explained and examined in past chapters and they should be drawn to the reader's attention.

The measurement of costs and returns on agricultural land over recent years does tend to over-emphasise the present-day characteristics of a stretch of farming countryside. Might not this be a weakness of the method in that land-use decisions made at a time of relative agricultural prosperity will over-emphasise the agricultural case whilst at times of farming depression the agricultural case, based as it is on a margin between value of output and cost of inputs at the particular point in time, will always appear to be weak? Thus, at the time of the severe agricultural depression in the early 1930's when even good farmers on the best land were making losses, the contribution of their land to the nation might be calculated as a very low quantity. Yet this good land and these good farmers were very valuable and very productive to the nation during the years of food shortage during the World Wars 1914–18 and 1939–45. Could it not then be said that these methods of evaluating the agricultural case in land-use planning do not allow for the potential value of land for food production?

This basic criticism draws attention to the need for using such methods of evaluation in a relative way and not as absolute standards. The siting technique, given in Chapter 5, is suggested only to show the size of the difference in agricultural value if more than one piece of agricultural land is being considered for urban use. Adjustments in the gross farm outputs and expenditure should be made to comply with the real situation over a number of years rather than giving a picture at one point in time. This can be done quite easily, as the discussion of the preparation of the Lymm evidence shows, by making adjustments in production and farm expenses from the records of changes taking place on farms of similar size and type collected regularly by the University Departments of Agricultural Economics. The results of these surveys are published in sufficient detail and frequently enough to be satisfactory for most major land-use controversies, especially if supplemented by local inquiries.

Again, changes in agricultural conditions through time will affect the situation on all of the agricultural sites being considered at any particular time, not on just one of them. The changes will not necessarily always penalise the good land. In fact, studies of farm incomes for many years have shown the strength and adaptability of the powerful combination of good land and good farmers using it—and the two certainly go together in most parts of the country and in many parts of the world. There are bound to be changes from time to time in the farming profitability of different enterprises, such as wheat growing as against milk production and fluctuations in factory type farming like pig and poultry production. These long-term fluctuations are important as they reflect changes in the relative need for different agricultural products.

It might be argued that city authorities, if forced to use the more expensive sites for urban development as a result of decisions based on techniques and concepts such as those suggested, should receive their extra capital and loans at reduced rates of interest. It might well be unfair to ask a local authority to obtain from local sources extra capital needed to implement a decision of a national nature though this is not a problem of interest rates but of social justice within the community. The rate of interest paid by a local authority or any moneys it borrows is at a level designed to attract capital away from other potential borrowers. If it borrows more or less than before and pays interest rates more or less than before, this means some less capital for other borrowers and some less interest for them to pay out. What is involved is really only a series of transfer payments from one part of the community to another part.

Many would argue that the incidence of any democratically agreed payments for the conservation of the better agricultural land should be on the general taxpayer and not on a local community directly concerned in a conservation decision. This is surely a matter of plain social and economic justice and its adoption would automatically reduce the powerful influence of local forces fighting for low local expenditure. The national costs of land conservation should certainly be kept away from the local ratepayer and they should be spread over the general body of taxpayers. This is just one facet of the politically and administratively difficult problem of compensation and betterment which many countries, including Great Britain, have so far failed to solve in relation to effective land planning.

Chapter 11 Conclusion

W E must not delude ourselves into thinking that the problems raised by the conflict and co-operation between agriculture and urban growth are unique to Great Britain. The growth of cities and their spread on to surrounding farm land is continuing all over the world—in places as different in their stage of development and in cultural and racial patterns as Accra in Ghana, Salisbury in Rhodesia, Ankara in Turkey, Delhi in India and Chicago in the United States. It is the largest cities that are growing at prodigious speed whether they are in highly or poorly developed countries. The only major difference between cities in the richer economies and those in the poorer is that the former are spilling out at a faster pace and the density of new development is generally much looser. For example, the New York metropolitan area is reputed to be expanding physically at the rate of 50 square miles a year and Los Angeles is already 50 miles in diameter. The pattern of what will occur in the towns or cities of the poorer countries as national and personal incomes rise is clear to see.

The position of the United States of America in this matter is fascinating. At the present time both the U.S.A. and England and Wales have roughly the same proportion of their land surface in non-agricultural and non-forestry uses —about one acre in every ten. But the statistics of land use in the U.S.A. are recorded and classified in very different ways from those in Great Britain and it would be unwise to push this comparison too far. In addition, the complaints we have made about the poor records kept of land-use change in Britain apply also to the United States. It can, however, be said that the Americans are already using much more land per person for their non-food needs, for their dwelling-places, transportation, commerce, military establishments and recreations, than are the Britons. It appears from the statistics that in comparison with the half an acre of urban land used by each American for such purposes, the Englishman has less than one-tenth of an acre. But the area under urban uses is increasing at the same pace in the U.S.A. as it is in England. Based on the estimates of change during the years 1945 to 1954, the spread of American cities and towns is of the order of not more than 1 per cent per annum. Our own estimates in England and Wales, based on town planning schemes, suggest an urban spread increasing at the rate of 1 to 2 per cent each year.

Although these American increases are very great, and the spread of urban areas there appears bewilderingly large to the visitor, estimates made by land economists in the United States suggest that, although their population will probably rise to 225,000,000 by 1975 and this will be accompanied by an increase in the non-agricultural area of from 183,600,000 acres (in 1954) to 204,900,000, the 1975 total will still be only 11 per cent of the total land area.[1]

The pattern and speed of urban growth in the United States at the present time needs to be studied by other countries as it is in that vast country that trends, common to all nations, are being allowed to work themselves out with a minimum of social control. The United States has today one of the fastest rates of population increase in the world. It is a country where there is a car, usually a large one, for each three persons, and a road network is being built of a size that will take this quantity of private transport. All the other appurtenances of modern living are conceived and implemented on a scale involving a lavish use of land— the new super-markets on the outskirts of the built-up areas with their large parking lots, the drive-in cinemas at the side of the main roads, the change from the apartment house and row of tenement dwellings to the individual detached house of a one-storey type on its own plot of land, the surface working of minerals and the setting aside of large areas for public and private recreation.

[1] United States Department of Agriculture, *Land*—the 1958 Yearbook of Agriculture, Washington, D.C., U.S.A., 1958.

This rapid change of land use is not going on unnoticed or undiscussed in the United States. Responsible investigators are not alarmed that the stock of good food-producing land is being seriously diminished although this question is now being raised in public discussion there. There is, however, concern at the scattered and spasmodic development taking place, with its heavy commitments in terms of the costly spread of physical and social services and access. The pattern and size of land values suggest that many individuals and financial interests are acting as if there were a potential shortage of land in the future in that country. Unused land in and close to cities and towns is remaining unused because of the high price asked. This forces development further out on to cheaper land and this land, because of poor and intermittent zoning ordinances, is often developed in a very spasmodic fashion. It is very often the easily worked, good agricultural land that is purchased and then broken into fragments, not so much because Americans like living on open flat land but because the sites have good access. The Americans, like the British, prefer to live on high and rolling sites but they are not able to use them chiefly because of poor access.

There are a number of other comparisons in the interactions of town growth and agriculture between the United States and Britain which are pertinent to the discussion in this book and the findings of the studies made in this country. Take, for example, the wastage of land preceding and accompanying urban growth. This has developed on a tremendous scale in North America. It is not a problem of human trespass on farms. The American is too fond of his car to be much of a wanderer in the countryside and he is somewhat more lucky than his English cousin in that large areas are available to him in State Parks, National Parks and in many other areas. The large stretches of land for recreation are used for few purposes. The National Park of Yellowstone, for example, is as large as the whole of Wales but its dominant uses are only two—tourists and wild life.

Lacking overall land planning schemes, the explosive effects of potential urban demand ramify widely into rural areas. A large amount of land is held vacant anticipating new higher value uses. In 1957 the United States Census reported that 13,000,000 vacant lots, excluding car parking spaces, were available for building. This was more than one-fifth of all city building lots and equivalent to thirteen times the annual consumption of land in new construction. Within existing urban areas, as well as on the fringes, there are great areas of unused land. For example, even in the 'crowded' city of San Francisco nearly a quarter of the land is under-developed and across the bay, in the 'solid mass' of suburbs like Oakland and Berkeley, more than half the land is unused.

The spectacle of greatest interest to anyone concerned with the use of rural land is the important switch from full to part-time farming in thickly populated areas and the large amount of land of second-rate farming quality which is going out of farming use altogether, especially in the eastern states. A typical situation can be described thus. Because of high prices for plots in or close to a city, a would-be buyer or builder of a private house considers living in a 'rural residence,' as it is called, within 50 miles of the city. The distance is much less of a handicap to an American than to a British worker because of higher salaries or wages, the fast large car and the good motor roads which allow unchecked fast speeds into the heart of most American cities. Because of high incomes on the better farm land and in city jobs, there is a migration of farmers from the poorer and smaller farms. These are then available at reasonable prices to city workers prepared to spend an hour or more a day travelling to and from town. A white framed house with a large barn and, perhaps a 'quarter section' (160 acres) of land is bought by such a man. He lives in the house, often making con-siderable improvements to it. The barn will house his one or two cars and a pony or so for the children. The land will probably be allowed to go back to natural scrub and wood-land with the exception, possibly, of one or two of the best fields where some part-time farming enterprise, involving very little labour, is carried on. And at the weekend the city dweller will enjoy his plot of wild countryside and the game which has come back in with the reversal of the land to its natural vegetation.

To what extent are these American trends of significance to Britain? Let us assume that this country does push ahead with its badly delayed main road improvement schemes so that speedy traffic in and out of the major cities is possible. This would mean that a private car travelling from, say 20 miles out, would be able to get regularly into the heart of a city in well under half an hour (and this is now the case with many American cities). The pressure for even more widespread urban dispersal will then be severe in Great Britain. It may well be linked with a greater development of part-time farming, particularly on smaller farms on difficult land because of the difficulties of making full-time incomes on such holdings. If such a development of part-time farming in certain regions of Britain does continue or accelerate, then the areas of rural land concerned are not likely to go derelict. Some may well be taken over by adjoining larger farms or turned, on part-time farms, to more extensive uses, such as the grazing of cattle and sheep.

It is obvious from what is happening in the rural areas which adjoin cities in most countries, that the accelerated development of the motor-car, the shorter working week and longer week-ends, and rising standards of living of large numbers of the population, will all result in a more lavish non-agricultural use of rural areas in Britain. The discussion of the national land-use pattern in Chapter 3 shows the relatively large amount of land used already by small settlements and isolated residences in this country as compared with towns and cities. It is also likely that considerable land wastage, from a point of view of food production, occurs if domestic gardens become very large. Survey work done on garden use also suggests, as mentioned in Chapter 7, that the gardens of privately owned houses grow much less in the way of fruit and vegetables than do those of State assisted houses. It is likely that the building of new private houses on the fringes of towns will become more important in relation to the construction of council houses as much of the attention and finance of local authorities will, it is hoped in the future, be involved in the redevelopment of some of the older and more crowded parts of British cities.

The general problems of urban growth have not been discussed in this book—only some of the interactions of agriculture and expanded towns. One of the most recent and readable accounts of the whole problem in Great Britain is *Cities in Flood*, by Peter Self,[1] where many facets of what has happened and is likely to happen are discussed. He deals with the nature and the strength of the pull of the large cities as places in which people decide to work and near which they want to live. These cities are now being subjected to explosive forces. There is an ever-increasing movement from the congested inner zones to suburban areas on the fringe as families try to combine good jobs with more private living space. A separation in space between where a person works and where he lives is becoming more and more the general custom and with it goes the difficulties of long daily journeys from home to work with the resulting expense, time lag and physical strain of travelling by road and rail. Self's suggestions for harnessing these forces for the general good include the control of employment in the big cities and the development of more jobs in distant places, the zoning of adequate and attractive space for future residential development and planning in advance to meet the needs of modern transport. In general he favours the development of more 'new' towns in the shape of substantial expansion to existing towns which are now only small or medium in size.

It is clear, therefore, that the impact of urban growth on rural and agricultural land will continue to be a vital problem. What are some of the more important elements of this problem emerging from our studies which deserve attention?

Early in this book we have tried to draw the reader's attention to the inadequacy of past and present records of changes in land use. Very few countries have suitable systems of recording land uses and changes therein, especially when judged against the increasing tempo of such change and the greater number of types of land uses now becoming important. Although the inadequacy of British land-use records is, therefore, only part of a general weakness seen in many

[1] Self, P., *Cities in Flood*, Faber, London, 1957.

countries, the particular weakness in the British records applies to their measurement of the land in agricultural or fringe agricultural uses. This is a serious weakness as agriculture is likely to continue as the dominant user of land in terms of physical area in all countries. Small percentage errors in its measurement therefore involve considerable acreages of land.

The responsibility for recording land uses should be centred in one Government department or institute with sufficient authority to impress its needs for adequate recording on to other Government departments and outside bodies interested only in one particular use of land. It is obvious, for example, that the Ministry of Agriculture, Fisheries and Food is much more interested in accurate measurement of the areas of productive crop land and numbers of farm livestock than in areas under fringe uses in the countryside, such as farm roads, yards and buildings, and the larger non-agricultural uses like woodland, rural roads, mineral workings and common land. Outside pressure and co-ordination will obviously be necessary to obtain complete records of rural land use as distinct from farm areas of productive agricultural land. Again, the Ministry of Fuel and Power is naturally much more interested and concerned in its records of the amounts and qualities of different minerals gained from its surface workings than in the area and type of land excavated. Acreage and surface details are more likely, therefore, if there is pressure from outside on such a specialised department to produce accurate land-use information.

The measurement of past and present land uses in Great Britain has proved to be a major task. The investigations have shown that the urban area of the country is rather smaller than was suggested by earlier estimates, the difference arising from weaknesses in measurement of the agricultural areas and the fact that, before Development Plans made under the Town and Country Planning Act of 1947 became available for study, the urban acreage had to be estimated as a residual use of land. This meant that errors in measuring the other major uses, such as agriculture and woodland, were automatically thrown into the total thought to be urban land.

The rate of increase in the area of urbanised land has been, however, rather greater than that suggested by earlier studies. Urban land represented only about five acres in every hundred in England and Wales in 1900. In the next twenty-five years it had only increased to 6 per cent. In the following quarter century, however, the area increased much more sharply, rising to nearly 10 acres in every 100 of the land surface by 1950.

It is also clear that this urban expansion is taking place on land with a much higher agricultural output than the average of all farm land and that the quality of the land being taken, as measured by value of output, is rising. The residential part of this new urban development may replace some part of this output of food through the contributions of the cultivated part of domestic gardens. There is, however, a marked difference between the character of food grown on the farm as compared with private gardens, and although the garden type of food production has proved useful in times of emergency (10 per cent of the total food output in the height of the domestic food-production campaign of the 1939–45 war) in the years since the war it is in foods which can only be produced on a farm scale, like beef, mutton and certain cereals, where extra output has been required in the national interest.

Because present and prospective urban development around the major urban centres of most countries involves high-grade agricultural land, better methods of assessing the national 'worth' of alternative sites for development are needed. Certain methods of comparative analysis have been suggested and their use demonstrated. There are, of course, many factors other than the value of the agricultural output and costs of building development that need to be balanced in making major land-use decisions. Some of these can be measured, but others have to depend on subjective judgements. It is encouraging that the idea of a planning balance sheet has recently been put forward by Lichfield,[1] in which a more systematic balancing of the case for and against each

[1] Lichfield, N., *The Economics of Planned Development*, Estates Gazette Ltd., London, 1956.

major case is shown to be valuable. In using an economic approach to the evaluation of the agricultural alternatives in town expansion and to major land reclamation and improvement schemes in the hills and lowlands, a number of methods of measurement are suggested. They include the food replacement concept. This represents an attempt to measure the capital costs of various schemes of land reclamation and improvement in relation to the replacement of the value of the output of the agricultural land earmarked for future urban growth. It is suggested that the replacement of this 'lost' output should be sought within home land resources rather than being obtained from abroad.

The value of the agricultural production of each acre zoned for future urban use varies from year to year and from one type of farming to another but the size of it can be calculated from the annual publications on farm incomes issued by the Ministry of Agriculture, Fisheries and Food. The weighted average, for example, in 1955–6 was £41 per acre, which is the production off that acre, net of purchases of feeding stuffs, seeds and animals. Using this figure, the relative capital costs of different types of land reclamation and improvement have been calculated from various studies made by other persons and specially at Wye College. The range of possible alternatives, in terms of their use of the capital resources of the whole community, is shown in Table 23.

What is the value of such an appraisal? The figures are only rough measures as suitable information is available only in a patchy or incomplete form. They do, however, throw some light on the relative size of the problem of food replacement and a use has been made of the concept in the evaluation of the worth of the agricultural land at Lymm, in north Cheshire, that has been under active consideration as a new town site. This has been done in order to get some idea of the amounts of capital it would be reasonable for the nation to expend on developing at higher urban densities or on sites of lower agricultural value in order to leave such good quality farm land in its agricultural use. Another method, using a social rate of discount in order to capitalise

H

Table 23

THE CAPITAL COST OF VARIOUS TYPES OF AGRICULTURAL
IMPROVEMENT IN TERMS OF FOOD REPLACEMENT

Type of agricultural improvement	Capital cost of food replacement per urbanised acre at 1955–6 values £'s	Return on capital invested in the improvement %
General intensification of agricultural production	165	13·8
Comprehensive improvement of livestock rearing farms on the hills and uplands	351	4 to 5
Reclamation of derelict woodland to agriculture	127	24
Coastal reclamation to agricultural use	118 to 225	2½ to 10
Reclaimed dry sand and gravel pits	137	10
Reclamation to agriculture of opencast coal and ironstone workings	820 to 3772	below 1·4

the value added by the agricultural use of a piece of land, has also been suggested for consideration.

The rates of return on capital, given in Table 23, are a customary method of measuring the value of a particular form of agricultural improvement, both in relation to the general level of interest rates and as between alternative schemes. The 'cost' of urbanisation of certain agricultural land cannot, however, be measured in this way.

The food replacement costs are not inversely related to the rate earned on capital, as a superficial glance at Table 23 might suggest, because of variations in the agricultural productivity of the different forms of improvement as compared with the productivity of the farm land earmarked for urban use. For example, the relatively low food replacement figure for coastal reclamation to agricultural use is not accompanied by high rates of return on capital. This is because of the high physical productivity of the reclaimed land when in full agricultural use, a productivity even higher than the average of the land earmarked for urban use. Again, the value of the agricultural output on livestock rearing farms in the hills is still relatively low, on a per acre basis, even after the degree of improvement thought possible has been made.

In straightforward comparisons of one type of agricultural land improvement with another, as, for example, the reclamation of areas on the coast as against derelict woodland, the rate of interest earned on the extra capital invested can be used. Here our work has shown that high rates of return are possible with expensive schemes of land reclamation if the land so gained can be fitted into the economy of a nearby farm without major increases in the fixed equipment of that farm. In contrast, rates of return on the capital involved are both slower to arrive and lower when the new land has to be equipped as new and additional farm units.

A major choice in agricultural development is between using more intensively the land already in cultivation or bringing into production newly reclaimed pieces of land. Our discussion of these alternatives suggests that the bringing in of new pieces of land which can be farmed with existing farm units looks at least as economic a proposition in this country as attempts at intensification of existing farms. In practice, new pieces of land can often be woven into the farm system without requiring any major change in the existing policy of the farmer. Intensification of existing land use, however, usually means moving from a simpler farm system to a more complicated one or, at least, improving standards of husbandry. This type of improvement usually involves higher skills in management. As in so many industries, a farm business remains small because of personal difficulties of the owner and manager in handling the greater complications and risks of a bigger business. An expanded business only becomes more efficient if the quality of its management also improves.

The range shown in Table 23 is great enough to suggest a lack of reconciliation between the rewards to be obtained from various major schemes of agricultural improvement and the expense involved in different forms of food replacement. There is a real need for more cost-benefit analyses of alternative forms of land reclamation and improvement. This is becoming more and more important as grants of a specific nature increase in the total of Government support to agriculture. As a nation we are spending many millions of pounds annually on specific improvements which are thought worth while (Table 24). A few thousand pounds spent on analyses as to whether or not they were proving worth while in their operation would surely be a wise investment! For example, further studies of the results of financial help on drainage, the provision of water supplies and to hill and livestock rearing land are surely needed.

Very few such studies are being made at the present time, at least as judged by the published reports of Government Departments and Universities. It is probable that suitable records of the results achieved are not being obtained by the administrators of such schemes because, firstly, arrangements to get them have not been made and, secondly, no consistent scheme of analysis has been agreed.

. Table 24

EXPENDITURE ON SOME OF THE MORE IMPORTANT PRODUCTION GRANTS TO AGRICULTURE—UNITED KINGDOM

Nature of grant	1955–6 expenditure £'000s	1958–9 estimates £'000s
Ploughing up	5,436	9,420
Land drainage and water supply............	2,776	2,622
Hill land, marginal production scheme and bracken eradication	1,651	2,227
Lime	10,237	9,750
Fertilisers	14,300	26,750
Livestock rearing land	1,470	1,676
Hill sheep and cattle.....................	3,742	2,880
Calf rearing	7,661	12,725

Source: 'A Record of Agricultural Policy,' Edith H. Whetham and Jean I. Currie, Occasional Paper No. 5. Farm Economics Branch, School of Agriculture, Cambridge University, December 1958, Part III, Table IV, p. 16.

The attempts at evaluation made in this book do, it is suggested, support the case for better records and more and better schemes of appraisal. Without them, piecemeal measures of grant aid to agriculture will also involve a real lack of knowledge about the relative value of each particular measure of support. Without them, arguments as to the desirability of certain areas of agricultural land for other purposes will continue to flounder in a morass of unrelated and emotional detail. If, for example, the Ministries of Agriculture and of Housing and Local Government feel that they cannot perform such tasks of evaluation, then the necessary funds and suitable types of records could be made available to independent investigators to carry out the work. Surely major decisions in land use and on grant-aided agricultural improvements are too vital to this country's well-being to be left without adequate appraisal on a cost-benefit basis?

It is realised that only certain aspects of the interrelationships between agriculture and the urbanisation of modern communities have been explored. But we have tried to concentrate on those aspects which are still somewhat neglected in land use planning in order to show that, by emphasising the importance of alternatives in land and food policies and the need for cost-benefit analyses, a more rational welding of different interests into a balanced use of the country's land resources can be made. Our emphasis on the economic and measurable aspects of the problem has been deliberate —not in order to suggest that the social, amenity and other non-economic aspects of wise land use are unimportant— but in order to strengthen the land planning mechanism by trying, at least as far as agriculture is concerned, to add more objectivity and rational measurement.

The explorations made have been patchy, and incomplete, but it is hoped that the picture of past and future land-use changes in Britain is somewhat clearer as a result of our work and that the interrelationships of town and country are reflected in a different and somewhat sharper light.

SELECTED BIBLIOGRAPHY

The following publications, some in book form and others in contributed articles, are particularly relevant to the general argument of the book.

Land Economics—General

BARLOWE, R., *Land Resource Economics*, Prentice-Hall, New Jersey, 1958.

ELY, R. T., and WEHRWEIN, G. S., *Land Economics*, Macmillan, New York, 1940.

JOHNSON, V. W., and BARLOWE, R., *Land Problems and Policies*, McGraw-Hill, New York, 1954.

LICHFIELD, N., *The Economics of Planned Development*, Estates Gazette Ltd., London, 1957.

RENNE, R. R., *Land Economics*, Revised Edition, Harper, New York, 1958.

TURVEY, R., *The Economics of Real Property*, Allen & Unwin, Ltd., London, 1957.

United States Department of Agriculture, *Land—Yearbook of Agriculture*, Washington, U.S.A., 1958.

Land Competition

Agricultural Land Service Research Group, 'Planned Urban Development and its Effect on Agriculture,' *Journal of the Town Planning Institute*, **39**, September–October 1953, pp. 234–7.

Agricultural Land Service, Ministry of Agriculture, Fisheries and Food, London, *Warwickshire—A Study of the Loss of Agricultural Land for Urban Development*, Technical Report No. 4, 1958.

BEST, R. H., and WARD, J. T., *The Garden Controversy*, Studies in Rural Land Use, No. 2, Wye College (University of London), 1956.

STAMP, L. D., 'Planning and Agriculture,' *Journal of the Town Planning Institute*, **36**, March–April 1950, pp. 141–52.

WARD, J. T., 'The Siting of Urban Development on Agricultural Land,' *Journal of Agricultural Economics*, Great Britain, **12**, December 1957, pp. 451–66.

WIBBERLEY, G. P., 'The Challenge of Rural Land Losses,' *Journal of the Royal Society of Arts*, **102,** July 1954, pp. 650–70.

WIBBERLEY, G. P., *Rural Land Policies in an Urban Britain*, Town and Country Planning Summer School, Report of Proceedings at St. Andrews University, 1954, Town Planning Institute, London, pp. 66–78.

WIBBERLEY, G. P., 'Land Planning and Agriculture,' *Journal of the Land Agents' Society*, London, **57,** March 1958, pp. 122–31.

Land Utilisation and Conservation

BEST, R. H., *The Major Land Uses of Great Britain*, Studies in Rural Land Use, No. 4, Wye College (University of London), 1959.

BEST, R. H., 'The Urban Area of Great Britain—An Estimate of the Extent of Urban Land in 1950,' *The Town Planning Review*, University of Liverpool, **28,** October 1957, pp. 191–208.

BEST, R. H., 'The Composition of the Urban Area in England and Wales,' *Journal of the Town Planning Institute*, London, **44,** June, 1958, pp. 160–4.

Forestry Commission, *Post-War Forest Policy*, Her Majesty's Stationery Office, Cmd. 6447, London, 1943.

HART, J. F., *The British Moorlands*, University of Georgia Monographs, No. 2, Athens, Georgia, U.S.A., 1955.

Ministry of Works and Planning, *Report of the Committee on Land Utilisation in Rural Areas* (*Scott Report*), Her Majesty's Stationery Office, Cmd. 6378, London, 1942.

STAMP, L. D., *The Land of Britain—Its Use and Misuse*, 2nd Edition, Longmans, London, 1950.

WIBBERLEY, G. P., *The Recent History of Land Use*, The Biological Productivity of Britain, Institute of Biology, London, 1958.

Agricultural Policy and World Food Supplies

BLAGBURN, C. H., 'Import Replacement by British Agriculture,' *Economic Journal*, **60,** March 1950, pp. 19–45.

NASH, E. F., 'The Competitive Position of British Agriculture,' *Journal of Agricultural Economics*, Great Britain, **11**, No. 3, June 1955, pp. 222–41.

Political and Economic Planning, *World Population and Resources*, London, 1955.

RAEBURN, J. R., 'Agricultural Policy—Some Economic Results and Prospects,' *Three Banks Review*, No. 20, December 1953, pp. 3–20.

ROBINSON, A., Articles on the future of British Foreign Trade, *Three Banks Review*, Edinburgh, No. 17, March 1953; No. 21, March 1954; No. 26, June 1955; No. 40, December 1958.

RUSSELL, E. J., *World Population and World Food Supplies*, Allen & Unwin, Ltd. London, 1954.

STAMP, L. D., *Our Undeveloped World*, Faber & Faber, London, 1953.

WATSON, J. S. (Editor), *Agriculture in the British Economy*, Proceedings of Conference, Imperial Chemical Industries, London, 1957.

Agricultural Land Improvement and Reclamation

Agricultural Land Service, Ministry of Agriculture, Fisheries and Food, *Lancashire—A Survey of the Uncultivated Lowland Moss Areas*, Technical Report No. 3, 1958.

Agricultural Land Service, Ministry of Agriculture, and Wye College, *The Reclamation of Derelict Woodland for Agricultural Use*, Technical Report No. 1, 1957.

ASHBY, A. W., and BRITTON, D. K., *Britain's 'Marginal' Land*, Scottish Agriculture, Department of Agriculture for Scotland, 31, 1951–2.

BEAVER, S. H., 'Land Reclamation after Surface Mineral Workings,' *Journal of the Town Planning Institute*, London, **41**, May 1955, pp. 146–54.

DAVIDSON, B. R., and WIBBERLEY, G. P., *The Agricultural Significance of the Hills*, Studies in Rural Land Use, No. 3, Wye College (University of London), 1956.

ELLISON, W., *Marginal Land in Britain*, Geoffrey Bles, London, 1953.

ELLISON, W., and BOYD, D. A., 'The Possibilities of Marginal

Land Reclamation: Some Results of a Survey in England and Wales,' *Journal of the Royal Agricultural Society of England*, **113**, 1952, pp. 26–43.

ELLISON, W., BOYD, D. A., and CHURCH, B. M., 'The Progress of Improvement on Upland and Hill Farms in England and Wales,' *Journal of the Royal Agricultural Society of England*, **116**, 1955, pp. 34–49.

Ministry of Agriculture, Fisheries and Food, *Mid-Wales Investigation Report*, Her Majesty's Stationery Office, Cmd. 9631, London, 1955.

Ministry of Housing and Local Government, London, *Derelict Land and its Reclamation*, Technical Memorandum No. 7, 1956.

Natural Resources (Technical) Committee, *Forestry, Agriculture and Marginal Land*, Her Majesty's Stationery Office, London, 1957.

Report of the Royal Commission on Common Land, 1955–58, Her Majesty's Stationery Office, Cmd. 462, London, 1958.

STAPLEDON, R. G., *The Land—Now and Tomorrow*, Faber & Faber, London, 1935.

WIBBERLEY, G. P., 'Some Aspects of Problem Rural Areas in Britain,' *Geographical Journal*, London, **120**, March 1954, pp. 43–58.

Urban Growth and Land Planning

CLARK, C., 'Transport—Maker and Breaker of Cities,' *The Town Planning Review*, University of Liverpool, **28**, January 1958, pp. 237–50.

GILLIE, F. B., and HUGHES, P. L., *Some Principles of Land Planning*, Liverpool University Press, Great Britain, 1950.

JAMES, J. R., 'Land Planning in an Expanding Economy,' *Journal of the Royal Society of Arts*, London, **106**, July 1958, pp. 589–604.

SELF, P., *Cities in Flood*, Faber & Faber, London, 1957.

WRIGHT, H. M., 'The Next Thirty Years,' *The Town Planning Review*, University of Liverpool, **27**, October 1956, pp. 103–23.

INDEX